13+T

THE FACE OF A NATION

BOOKS BY THOMAS WOLFE

The Web and the Rock

The Story of a Novel

From Death to Morning

Of Time and the River

Look Homeward, Angel

THE FACE
OF A
NATION

Poetical Passages
From the Writings
of

THOMAS WOLFE

Decorations by
EDWARD SHENTON

CHARLES SCRIBNER'S SONS · NEW YORK
1939

Introduction

by John Hall Wheelock

For all his huge frame, his great force, there was something childlike about Thomas Wolfe. He amazed his friends as often by his naïveté as by those sudden flashes of insight, of phenomenal awareness, that characterized his talk. We were accustomed to surprises from Tom, but of all the things I was to hear him say, none, I think, amazed me more than his remark, vehemently flung out one day and often repeated later: "I'd rather be a poet than anything else in the world. God, what wouldn't I give to be one!" And it was true. No man loved poetry with a deeper passion, or lived with it more constantly, than Tom. What was incredible was the fact that a born poet, the author of some of the most magnificent dithyrambic passages in literature, should not know himself as such, should seem to define poetry by the narrow conventions of verse, something that was a matter of form rather than of spirit.

Now, with the passage of time, it becomes clear that, whatever else he may have been or achieved, Thomas Wolfe was, first of all, a poet—a lyric poet of extraordinary intensity, with a sensitivity to word-music, to rhythm and cadence, which can be likened only to that of Whitman, whose vision of America and of the American continent he shared. The American spirit and the American earth of our day as distinguished from the spirit and earth of any other land or time, these are the major

[v]

themes of Wolfe's writing, and it is as a poet that he articulates them. In so doing he has given many Americans a fresh sense of their country.

The selections from Wolfe's various volumes here brought together have been confined as strictly as possible to those passages, capable of standing alone, where he speaks purely as a poet. Some are many pages in length, others contain but a few lines, and the mood varies from the nostalgic and sombre to the satiric or, occasionally, even the humorous. Where long lyrical stretches were interrupted by snatches of dialogue or narrative matter, these apparently incongruous interludes have been retained for the purposes of contrast and relief which so obviously they are intended to serve.

It is not possible to read the selections here included without coming to a fresh realization of the genius of Thomas Wolfe. The essential Thomas Wolfe is here, and he is a poet. In these pages, Tom's wish to be a poet rather than anything else in the world is gloriously fulfilled.

JOHN HALL WHEELOCK

Contents

CONTENTS

CONTENTS

[ix]

CONTENTS

CONTENTS

CONTENTS

THE FACE OF *A* NATION

America

AMERICA has a thousand lights and weathers and we walk the streets, we walk the streets forever, we walk the streets of life alone.

It is the place of the howling winds, the hurrying of the leaves in old October, the hard clean falling to the earth of acorns. The place of the storm-tossed moaning of the wintry mountainside, where the young men cry out in their throats and feel the savage vigor, the rude strong energies; the place also where the trains cross rivers.

It is a fabulous country, the only fabulous country; it is the one place where miracles not only happen, but where they happen all the time.

It is the place of exultancy and strong joy, the place of the darkened brooding air, the smell of snow; it is the place of all the fierce, the bitten colors in October, when all of the wild, sweet woods flame up; it is also the place of the cider press and the last brown oozings of the York Imperials. It is the place of the lovely girls with good jobs and the husky voices, who will buy a round of drinks; it is the place where the women with fine legs and silken underwear lie in the pullman berth below you, it is the place of the dark-green snore of the pullman cars, and the voices in the night-time in Virginia.

It is the place where great boats are baying at the harbor's mouth, where great ships are putting out to sea; it is the place where great boats are blowing in the gulf of night, and where the river, the dark and secret river, full of strange time, is forever flowing by us to the sea.

The tugs keep baying in the river; at twelve o'clock the Berengaria *moans, her lights slide gently past the piers beyond Eleventh Street; and in the night a tall tree falls in Old Catawba, there in the hills of home.*

It is the place of autumnal moons hung low and
orange at the frosty edges of the pines; it is the place
of frost and silence; of the clean dry shocks and the
opulence of enormous pumpkins that yellow on hard
clotted earth; it is the place of the stir and feathery
stumble of the hens upon their roost, the frosty, broken
barking of the dogs, the great barn-shapes and solid
shadows in the running sweep of the moon-whited countryside, the wailing whistle of the fast express. It is the
place of flares and steamings on the tracks, and the
swing and bob and tottering dance of lanterns in the
yards; it is the place of dings and knellings and the
sudden glare of mighty engines over sleeping faces in
the night; it is the place of the terrific web and spread
and smouldering, the distant glare of Philadelphia and
the solid rumble of the sleepers; it is also the place where
the Transcontinental Limited is stroking eighty miles
an hour across the continent and the small dark towns
whip by like bullets, and there is only the fanlike stroke
of the secret, immense and lonely earth again.

*I have foreseen this picture many times: I will buy
passage on the Fast Express.*

It is the place of the wild and exultant winter's morning and the wind, with the powdery snow, that has been
howling all night long; it is the place of solitude and
the branches of the spruce and hemlock piled with
snow; it is the place where the Fall River boats are
tethered to the wharf, and the wild gray snow of furious, secret, and storm-whited morning whips across
them. It is the place of the lodge by the frozen lake

and the sweet breath and amorous flesh of sinful woman; it is the place of the tragic and lonely beauty of New England; it is the place of the red barn and the sound of the stabled hooves and of bright tatters of old circus posters; it is the place of the immense and pungent smell of breakfast, the country sausages and the ham and eggs, the smoking wheat cakes and the fragrant coffee, and of lonely hunters in the frosty thickets who whistle to their lop-eared hounds.

Where is old Doctor Ballard now with all his dogs? He held that they were sacred, that the souls of all the dear lost dead went into them. His youngest sister's soul sat on the seat beside him; she had long ears and her eyes were sad. Two dozen of his other cherished dead trotted around the buggy as he went up the hill past home. And that was eleven years ago, and I was nine years old; and I stared gravely out the window of my father's house at old Doctor Ballard.

It is the place of the straight stare, the cold white bellies and the buried lust of the lovely Boston girls; it is the place of ripe brainless blondes with tender lips and a flowery smell, and of the girls with shapely arms who stand on ladders picking oranges; it is also the place where large slow-bodied girls from Kansas City, with big legs and milky flesh, are sent East to school by their rich fathers, and there are also immense and lovely girls, with the grip of a passionate bear, who have such names as Neilson, Lundquist, Jorgenson, and Brandt.

I will go up and down the country, and back and forth across the country on the great trains that thun-

*der over America. I will go out West where States are
square; Oh, I will go to Boise, and Helena and Albu-
querque. I will go to Montana and the two Dakotas
and the unknown places.*

It is the place of violence and sudden death; of the
fast shots in the night, the club of the Irish cop, and
the smell of brains and blood upon the pavement; it
is the place of the small-town killings, and the men who
shoot the lovers of their wives; it is the place where the
negroes slash with razors and the hillmen kill in the
mountain meadows; it is the place of the ugly drunks
and the snarling voices and of foul-mouthed men who
want to fight; it is the place of the loud word and the
foolish boast and the violent threat; it is also the place
of the deadly little men with white faces and the eyes
of reptiles, who kill quickly and casually in the dark;
it is the lawless land that feeds on murder.

*"Did you know the two Lipe girls?" he asked. "Yes,"
I said. "They lived in Biltburn by the river, and one of
them was drowned in the flood. She was a cripple, and
she wheeled herself along in a chair. She was strong as
a bull." "That's the girl," he said.*

It is the place of the crack athletes and of the runners
who limber up in March; it is the place of the ten-
second men and the great jumpers and vaulters; it is
the place where Spring comes, and the young birch
trees have white and tender barks, of the thaw of the
earth, and the feathery smoke of the trees; it is the
place of the burst of grass and bud, the wild and sudden
tenderness of the wilderness, and of the crews out on the

river and the coaches coming down behind them in the motor-boats, the surges rolling out behind when they are gone with heavy sudden wash. It is the place of the baseball players, and the easy lob, the soft spring smackings of the glove and mitt, the crack of the bat; it is the place of the great batters, fielders, and pitchers, of the nigger boys and the white, drawling, shirt-sleeved men, the bleachers and the resinous smell of old worn wood; it is the place of Rube Waddell, the mighty untamed and ill-fated pitcher when his left arm is swinging like a lash. It is the place of the fighters, the crafty Jewish lightweights and the mauling Italians, Leonard, Tendler, Rocky Kansas, and Dundee; it is the place where the champion looks over his rival's shoulder with a bored expression.

I shall wake at morning in a foreign land thinking I heard a horse in one of the streets of home.

It is the place where they like to win always, and boast about their victories; it is the place of quick money and sudden loss; it is the place of the mile-long freights with their strong, solid, clanking, heavy loneliness at night, and of the silent freight of cars that curve away among raw piney desolations with their promise of new lands and unknown distances—the huge attentive gape of emptiness. It is the place where the bums come singly from the woods at sunset, the huge stillness of the water-tower, the fading light, the rails, secret and alive, and trembling with the oncoming train; it is the place of the great tramps, Oklahoma Red, Fargo Pete, and

[6]

the Jersey Dutchman, who grab fast rattlers for the
Western shore; it is the place of old blown bums who
come up in October skirls of dust and wind and crum-
pled newspapers and beg, with canned heat on their
breaths: "Help Old McGuire: McGuire's a good guy,
kid. You're not so tough, kid: McGuire's your pal,
kid: How about McGuire, McGuire——?"

It is the place of the poolroom players and the drug-
store boys; of the town whore and her paramour, the
tough town driver; it is the place where they go to the
woods on Sunday and get up among the laurel and
dogwood bushes and the rhododendron blossoms; it is
the place of the cheap hotels and the kids who wait with
chattering lips while the nigger goes to get them their
first woman; it is the place of the drunken college boys
who spend the old man's money and wear fur coats to
the football games; it is the place of the lovely girls up
North who have rich fathers, of the beautiful wives of
business men.

*The train broke down somewhere beyond Manassas,
and I went forward along the tracks with all the other
passengers. "What's the matter?" I said to the engineer.
"The eccentric strap is broken, son," he said. It was a
very cold day, windy and full of sparkling sun. This was
the farthest north I'd ever been, and I was twelve years
old and on my way to Washington to see Woodrow
Wilson inaugurated. Later, I could not forget the face
of the engineer and the words "eccentric strap."*

It is the place of the immense and lonely earth, the

[7]

place of fat ears and abundance where they grow cotton, corn, and wheat, the wine-red apples of October, and the good tobacco.

It is the place that is savage and cruel, but it is also the innocent place; it is the wild lawless place, the vital earth that is soaked with the blood of the murdered men, with the blood of the countless murdered men, with the blood of the unavenged and unremembered murdered men; but it is also the place of the child and laughter, where the young men are torn apart with ecstasy, and cry out in their throats with joy, where they hear the howl of the wind and the rain and smell the thunder and the soft numb spitting of the snow, where they are drunk with the bite and sparkle of the air and mad with the solar energy, where they believe in love and victory and think that they can never die.

It is the place where you come up through Virginia on the great trains in the night-time, and rumble slowly across the wide Potomac and see the morning sunlight on the nation's dome at Washington, and where the fat man shaving in the pullman washroom grunts, "What's this? What's this we're coming to—Washington?"—And the thin man glancing out the window says, "Yep, this is Washington. That's what it is, all right. You gettin' off here?"—And where the fat man grunts, "Who— me? Naw—I'm goin' on to Baltimore." It is the place where you get off at Baltimore and find your brother waiting.

Where is my father sleeping on the land? Buried? Dead these seven years? Forgotten, rotten in the ground? Held by his own great stone? No, no! Will I say, "Father" when I come to him? And will he call me, "Son"? Oh, no, he'll never see my face: we'll never speak except to say——

It is the place of the fast approach, the hot blind smoky passage, the tragic lonely beauty of New England, and the web of Boston; the place of the mighty station there, and engines passive as great cats, the straight dense plumes of engine smoke, the acrid and exciting smell of trains and stations, and of the man-swarm passing ever in its million-footed weft, the smell of the sea in harbors and the thought of voyages—and the place of the goat-cry, the strong joy of our youth, the magic city, when we knew the most fortunate life on earth would certainly be ours, that we were twenty and could never die.

And always America is the place of the deathless and enraptured moments, the eye that looked, the mouth that smiled and vanished, and the word; the stone, the leaf, the door we never found and never have forgotten. And these are the things that we remember of America, for we have known all her thousand lights and weathers, and we walk the streets, we walk the streets forever, we walk the streets of life alone.

The Golden World

HE HAD heard already the ringing of remote
church bells over a countryside on Sunday
night; had listened to the earth steeped in the
brooding symphony of dark, and the million-
noted little night things; and he had heard thus the far
retreating wail of a whistle in a distant valley, and faint
thunder on the rails; and he felt the infinite depth and
width of the golden world in the brief seductions of a
thousand multiplex and mixed mysterious odors and
sensations, weaving, with a blinding interplay and aural
explosions, one into the other.

He remembered yet the East India Tea House at
the Fair, the sandalwood, the turbans, and the robes,
the cool interior and the smell of India tea; and he had
felt now the nostalgic thrill of dew-wet mornings in

Spring, the cherry scent, the cool clarion earth, the wet loaminess of the garden, the pungent breakfast smells and the floating snow of blossoms. He knew the inchoate sharp excitement of hot dandelions in young Spring grass at noon; the smell of cellars, cobwebs, and built-on secret earth; in July, of watermelons bedded in sweet hay, inside a farmer's covered wagon; of cantaloupe and crated peaches; and the scent of orange rind, bitter-sweet, before a fire of coals. He knew the good male smell of his father's sitting-room; of the smooth worn leather sofa, with the gaping horse-hair rent; of the blistered varnished wood upon the hearth; of the heated calf-skin bindings; of the flat moist plug of apple to-bacco, stuck with a red flag; of wood-smoke and burnt leaves in October; of the brown tired autumn earth; of honey-suckle at night; of warm nasturtiums; of a clean ruddy farmer who comes weekly with printed butter, eggs and milk; of fat limp underdone bacon and of coffee; of a bakery-oven in the wind; of large deep-hued stringbeans smoking-hot and seasoned well with salt and butter; of a room of old pine boards in which books and carpets have been stored, long closed; of Concord grapes in their long white baskets.

Yes, and the exciting smell of chalk and varnished desks; the smell of heavy bread-sandwiches of cold fried meat and butter; the smell of new leather in a saddler's shop, or of a warm leather chair; of honey and of un-ground coffee; of barrelled sweet-pickles and cheese and all the fragrant compost of the grocer's; the smell of stored apples in the cellar, and of orchard-apple smells, of pressed-cider pulp; of pears ripening on a sunny shelf, and of ripe cherries stewing with sugar on hot stoves before preserving; the smell of whittled wood, of all young lumber, of sawdust and shavings; of peaches stuck with cloves and pickled in brandy; of pine-sap, and green pine-needles; of a horse's pared hoof; of chestnuts roasting, of bowls of nuts and raisins; of hot cracklin, and of young roast pork; of butter and cinnamon melting on hot candied yams.

Yes, and of the rank slow river, and of tomatoes rotten on the vine; the smell of rain-wet plums and boiling quinces; of rotten lily-pads; and of foul weeds rotting in green marsh scum; and the exquisite smell of the South, clean but funky, like a big woman; of soaking trees and the earth after heavy rain.

Yes, and the smell of hot daisy-fields in the morning; of melted puddling-iron in a foundry; the winter smell of horse-warm stables and smoking dung; of old oak and walnut; and the butcher's smell of meat, of strong slaughtered lamb, plump gouty liver, ground pasty sausages, and red beef; and of brown sugar melted with slivered bitter chocolate; and of crushed mint leaves, and of a wet lilac bush; of magnolia beneath the heavy moon, of dogwood and laurel; of an old caked pipe and Bourbon rye, aged in kegs of charred oak; the sharp smell of tobacco; of carbolic and nitric acids; the coarse true smell of a dog; of old imprisoned books; and the cool fern-smell near springs; of vanilla in cake-dough; and of cloven ponderous cheeses.

Yes, and of a hardware store. But mostly the good

smell of nails; of the developing chemicals in a photographer's dark-room; and the young-life smell of paint and turpentine; of buckwheat batter and black sorghum; and of a negro and his horse, together; of boiling fudge; the brine smell of pickling vats; and the lush undergrowth smell of southern hills; of a slimy oyster-can, of chilled gutted fish; of a hot kitchen negress; of kerosene and linoleum; of sarsaparilla and guavas; and of ripe autumn persimmons; and the smell of the wind and the rain; and of the acrid thunder; of cold starlight, and the brittle-bladed frozen grass; of fog and the misted winter sun; of seed-time, bloom, and mellow dropping harvest.

Greeting and Farewell

AND outside there was the raw and desolate-looking country, there were the great steel coaches, the terrific locomotives, the shining rails, the sweep of the tracks, the vast indifferent dinginess and rust of colors, the powerful mechanical expertness, and the huge indifference to suave finish. And inside there were the opulent green and luxury of the Pullman cars, the soft glow of the lights, and people fixed there for an instant in incomparably rich and vivid little pictures of their life and destiny, as they were all hurled onward, a thousand atoms, to their journey's end somewhere upon the mighty continent, across the immense and lonely visage of the everlasting earth.

And they looked at one another for a moment, they passed and vanished and were gone forever, yet it seemed to him that he had known these people, that he knew them better than the people in his own train, and that, having met them for an instant under immense and timeless skies, as they were hurled across the continent to a thousand destinations, they had met, passed, vanished, yet would remember this forever. And he thought the people in the two trains felt this, also: slowly they passed each other now, and their mouths smiled and their eyes grew friendly, but he thought there was some sorrow and regret in what they felt. For, having lived together as strangers in the immense and swarming city, they now had met upon the everlasting earth, hurled past each other for a moment between two points in time upon the shining rails, never to meet, to speak, to know each other any more, and the briefness of their days, the destiny of man, was in that instant greeting and farewell.

Fixity and Change

THE mountains were his masters. They rimmed
in life. They were the cup of reality, beyond
growth, beyond struggle and death. They were
his absolute unity in the midst of eternal
change. Old haunt-eyed faces glimmered in his memory. He thought of Swain's cow, St. Louis, death, himself in the cradle. He was the haunter of himself, trying
for a moment to recover what he had been part of. He
did not understand change, he did not understand
growth. He stared at his framed baby picture in the
parlor, and turned away sick with fear and the effort to
touch, retain, grasp himself for only a moment.

And these bodiless phantoms of his life appeared with
terrible precision, with all the mad nearness of a vision.
That which was five years gone came within the touch
of his hand, and he ceased at that moment to believe in

THE FACE OF A NATION

his own existence. He expected some one to wake him; he would hear Gant's great voice below the laden vines, would gaze sleepily from the porch into the rich low moon, and go obediently to bed. But still there would be all that he remembered before that and what if— Cause flowed ceaselessly into cause.

He heard the ghostly ticking of his life; his powerful clairvoyance, the wild Scotch gift of Eliza, burned inward back across the phantom years, plucking out of the ghostly shadows a million gleams of light—a little station by the rails at dawn, the road cleft through the pineland seen at twilight, a smoky cabin-light below the trestles, a boy who ran among the bounding calves, a wisp-haired slattern, with snuff-sticked mouth, framed in a door, floury negroes unloading sacks from freight-cars on a shed, the man who drove the Fair Grounds bus at Saint Louis, a cool-lipped lake at dawn.

His life coiled back into the brown murk of the past like a twined filament of electric wire; he gave life, a pattern, and movement to these million sensations that Chance, the loss or gain of a moment, the turn of the head, the enormous and aimless impulsion of accident, had thrust into the blazing heat of him. His mind picked out in white living brightness these pinpoints of experience and the ghostliness of all things else became more awful because of them. So many of the sensations that returned to open haunting vistas of fantasy and imagining had been caught from a whirling landscape through the windows of the train.

And it was this that awed him—the weird combina-

[17]

tion of fixity and change, the terrible moment of immobility stamped with eternity in which, passing life at great speed, both the observer and the observed seem frozen in time. There was one moment of timeless suspension when the land did not move, the train did not move, the slattern in the doorway did not move, he did not move. It was as if God had lifted his baton sharply above the endless orchestration of the seas, and the eternal movement had stopped, suspended in the timeless architecture of the absolute. Or like those motion-pictures that describe the movements of a swimmer making a dive, or a horse taking a hedge—movement is petrified suddenly in mid-air, the inexorable completion of an act is arrested. Then, completing its parabola, the suspended body plops down into the pool. Only, these images that burnt in him existed without beginning or ending, without the essential structure of time. Fixed in no-time, the slattern vanished, fixed, without a moment of transition.

His sense of unreality came from time and movement, from imagining the woman, when the train had passed, as walking back into the house, lifting a kettle from the hearth embers. Thus life turned shadow, the living lights went ghost again. The boy among the calves. Where later? Where now?

I am, he thought, a part of all that I have touched and that has touched me, which, having for me no existence save that which I gave to it, became other than itself by being mixed with what I then was, and is now still otherwise, having fused with what I now am, which is itself a cumulation of what I have been becoming. Why here? Why there? Why now? Why then?

Beyond all misuse, waste, pain, tragedy, death, confusion, unswerving necessity was on the rails; not a sparrow fell through the air but that its repercussion acted on his life, and the lonely light that fell upon the viscous and interminable seas at dawn awoke sea-changes washing life to him. The fish swam upward from the depth.

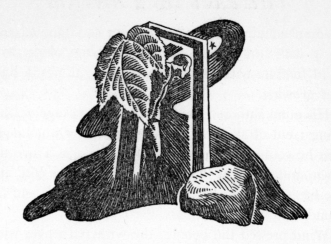

We Shall Not Come Again

THE great stars rode proudly up into heaven. And just over him, just over the town, it seemed, there was one so rich and low he could have touched it. Ben's grave had been that day freshly sodded: there was a sharp cold smell of earth there. Eugene thought of Spring, and the poignant and wordless odor of the elvish dandelions that would be there. In the frosty dark, far-faint, there was the departing wail of a whistle.

And suddenly, as he watched the lights wink cheerfully up in the town, their warm message of the hived life of men brought to him a numb hunger for all the words and the faces. He heard the far voices and laughter. And on the distant road a powerful car, bending around the curve, cast over him for a second, over that lonely hill of the dead, its great shaft of light and life. In his numbed mind, which for days now had fumbled curiously with little things, with little things alone, as a child fumbles with blocks or with little things, a light was growing.

His mind gathered itself out of the wreckage of little things: out of all that the world had shown or taught him he could remember now only the star above the town, and the light that had swung over the hill, and the fresh sod upon Ben's grave, and the wind, and far sounds and music, and Mrs. Pert.

Wind pressed the boughs, the withered leaves were shaking. It was October, but the leaves were shaking. A star was shaking. A light was waking. Wind was quaking. The star was far. The night, the light. The light was bright. A chant, a song, the slow dance of the little things within him. The star over the town, the light over the hill, the sod over Ben, night over all. His mind fumbled with little things. Over us all is something. Star, night, earth, light . . . light . . . O lost! . . . a stone . . . a leaf . . . a door . . . O ghost! . . . a light . . . a song . . . a light . . . a light swings over the hill . . . over us all . . . a star shines over the town . . . over us all . . . a light.

We shall not come again. We never shall come back again. But over us all, over us all, over us all is—something.

Wind pressed the boughs; the withered leaves were shaking. It was October, but some leaves were shaking.

A light swings over the hill. (We shall not come again.) And over the town a star. (Over us all, over us all that shall not come again.) And over the day the dark. But over the darkness—what?

We shall not come again. We never shall come back again.

Over the dawn a lark. (That shall not come again.) And wind and music far. O lost! (It shall not come again.) And over your mouth the earth. O ghost! But, over the darkness—what?

Wind pressed the boughs; the withered leaves were quaking.

We shall not come again. We never shall come back again. It was October, but we never shall come back again.

When will they come again? When will they come again?

The laurel, the lizard, and the stone will come no more. The women weeping at the gate have gone and will not come again. And pain and pride and death will pass, and will not come again. And light and dawn will pass, and the star and the cry of a lark will pass, and will not come again. And we shall pass, and shall not come again.

What things will come again? O Spring, the cruelest and fairest of the seasons, will come again. And the strange and buried men will come again, in flower and leaf the strange and buried men will come again, and death and the dust will never come again, for death and the dust will die. And Ben will come again, he will not die again, in flower and leaf, in wind and music far, he will come back again.

O lost, and by the wind grieved, ghost, come back again!

It had grown dark. The frosty night blazed with great brilliant stars. The lights in the town shone with sharp radiance. Presently, when he had lain upon the cold earth for some time, Eugene got up and went away toward the town.

Wind pressed the boughs; the withered leaves were shaking.

The Unvisited World

H E BELIEVED himself thus at the centre of life;
he believed the mountains rimmed the heart
of tne world; he believed that from all the
chaos of accident the inevitable event came at
the inexorable moment to add to the sum of his life.
Against the hidden other flanks of the immutable
hills the world washed like a vast and shadowy sea,
alive with the great fish of his imagining. Variety, in
this unvisited world, was unending, but order and purpose certain: there would be no wastage in adventure—
courage would be rewarded with beauty, talent with
success, all merit with its true deserving. There would
be peril, there would be toil, there would be struggle.
But there would not be confusion and waste. There
would not be groping. For collected Fate would fall, on

its chosen moment, like a plum. There was no disorder in enchantment.

Spring lay abroad through all the garden of this world. Beyond the hills the land bayed out to other hills, to golden cities, to rich meadows, to deep forests, to the sea. Forever and forever.

Beyond the hills were the mines of King Solomon, the toy republics of Central America, and little tinkling fountains in a court; beyond, the moonlit roofs of Bagdad, the little grated blinds of Samarkand, the moonlit camels of Bythinia, the Spanish ranch-house of the Triple Z, and J. B. Montgomery and his lovely daughter stepping from their private car upon a western track; and the castle-haunted crags of Graustark; the fortune-yielding casino of Monte Carlo; and the blue eternal Mediterranean, mother of empires. And instant wealth ticked out upon a tape, and the first stage of the Eiffel Tower where the restaurant was, and Frenchmen setting fire to their whiskers, and a farm in Devon, white cream, brown ale, the winter's chimney merriment, and *Lorna Doone;* and the hanging gardens of Babylon, and supper in the sunset with the queens, and the slow slide of the barge upon the Nile, or the wise rich bodies of Egyptian women couched on moonlit balustrades, and the thunder of the chariots of great kings, and tomb-treasure sought at midnight, and the wine-rich chateau land of France, and calico warm legs in hay.

Upon a field in Thrace Queen Helen lay, her lovely body dappled in the sun.

Where Now?

W HERE now?" Under such a heading as this, there would be brief notations of those thousands of things which all of us have seen for just a flash, a moment in our lives, which seem to be of no consequence whatever at the moment that we see them, and which live in our minds and hearts forever, which are somehow pregnant with all the joy and sorrow of the human destiny, and which we know, somehow, are therefore more important than many things of more apparent consequence. "Where now?" Some quiet steps that came and passed along a leafy night-time street in summer in a little town down South long years ago; a woman's voice, her sudden burst of low and tender laughter; then the voices and the footsteps going, silence, the leafy rustle of the trees. "Where now?" Two trains that met and paused at a little station at some little town at some unknown moment upon the huge body of the continent; a girl who looked and smiled from the window of the other train; another passing in a motor car on the streets of Norfolk; the winter boarders in a little boarding house down South twenty years ago; Miss Florrie

Mangle, the trained nurse; Miss Jessie Rimmer, the cashier at Reed's drug store; Doctor Richards, the clairvoyant; the pretty girl who cracked the whip and thrust her head into the lion's mouth with Johnny J. Jones' Carnival and Combined Shows.

"Where now?" It went beyond the limits of man's actual memory. It went back to the farthest adyt of his childhood before conscious memory had begun, the way he thought he must have felt the sun one day and heard Peagram's cow next door wrenching the coarse grass against the fence, or heard the street car stop upon the hill above his father's house at noon; and Earnest Peagram coming home to lunch, his hearty voice in midday greeting; and then the street car going, the sudden lonely green-gold silence of the street car's absence and an iron gate slamming, then the light of that lost day fades out. "Where now?" He can recall no more and does not know if what he has recalled is fact or fable or a fusion of the two. Where now—in these great ledger books, month after month, I wrote such things as this, not only the concrete, material record of man's ordered memory, but all the things he scarcely dares to think he has remembered; all the flicks and darts and haunting lights that flash across the mind of man that will return unbidden at an unexpected moment: a voice once heard; a face that vanished; the way the sunlight came and went; the rustling of a leaf upon a bough; a stone, a leaf, a door.

Conversation by Moonlight

THE Square lay under blazing moonlight. The fountain pulsed with a steady breezeless jet: the water fell upon the pool with a punctual slap. No one came into the Square.

The chimes of the bank's clock struck the quarter

after three as Eugene entered from the northern edge, by Academy Street.

He came slowly over past the fire department and the City Hall. On Gant's corner, the Square dipped sharply down toward Niggertown, as if it had been bent at the edge.

Eugene saw his father's name, faded, on the old brick in moonlight. On the stone porch of the shop, the angels held their marble posture. They seemed to have frozen, in the moonlight.

Leaning against the iron railing of the porch, above the sidewalk, a man stood smoking. Troubled and a little afraid, Eugene came over. Slowly, he mounted the long wooden steps, looking carefully at the man's face. It was half-obscured in shadow.

"Is there anybody there?" said Eugene.

No one answered.

But, as Eugene reached the top, he saw that the man was Ben.

Ben stared at him a moment without speaking. Although Eugene could not see his face very well under the obscuring shadow of his gray felt hat, he knew that he was scowling.

"Ben?" said Eugene doubtfully, faltering a little on the top step. "Is it you, Ben?"

"Yes," said Ben. In a moment, he added in a surly voice: "Who did you think it was, you little idiot?"

"I wasn't sure," said Eugene somewhat timidly. "I couldn't see your face."

They were silent a moment. Then Eugene, clearing his throat in his embarrassment, said: "I thought you were dead, Ben."

"Ah-h!" said Ben contemptuously, jerking his head sharply upward. "Listen to this, won't you?"

He drew deeply on his cigarette: the spiral fumes coiled out and melted in the moon-bright silence.

"No," he said in a moment, quietly. "No, I'm not dead."

Eugene came up on the porch and sat down on a limestone base, up-ended. Ben turned, in a moment, and climbed up on the rail, bending forward comfortably upon his knees.

Eugene fumbled in his pockets for a cigarette, with fingers that were stiff and trembling. He was not frightened: he was speechless with wonder and strong eagerness, and afraid to betray his thoughts to ridicule. He lighted a cigarette. Presently he said, painfully, hesitantly, in apology:

"Ben, are you a ghost?"

Ben did not mock.

"No," he said. "I am not a ghost."

There was silence again, while Eugene sought timorously for words.

"I hope," he began presently, with a small cracked laugh, "I hope, then, this doesn't mean that I'm crazy?"

"Why not?" said Ben, with a swift flickering grin. "Of course you're crazy."

"Then," said Eugene slowly, "I'm imagining all this?"

"In heaven's name!" Ben cried irritably. "How should I know? Imagining all what?"

"What I mean," said Eugene, "is, are we here talking together, or not?"

"Don't ask me," said Ben. "How should I know?"

With a strong rustle of marble and a cold sigh of weariness, the angel nearest Eugene moved her stone foot and lifted her arm to a higher balance. The slender lily stipe shook stiffly in her elegant cold fingers.

"Did you see that?" Eugene cried excitedly.

"Did I see what?" said Ben, annoyed.

"Th-th-that angel there!" Eugene chattered, pointing with a trembling finger. "Did you see it move? It lifted its arm."

"What of it?" Ben asked irritably. "It has a right to, hasn't it? You know," he added with biting sarcasm, "there's no law against an angel lifting its arm if it wants to."

"No, I suppose not," Eugene admitted slowly, after a moment. "Only, I've always heard——"

"Ah! Do you believe all you hear, fool?" Ben cried fiercely. "Because," he added more calmly, in a moment, drawing on his cigarette, "you're in a bad way if you do."

There was again silence while they smoked. Then Ben said:

"When are you leaving, 'Gene?"

"To-morrow," Eugene answered.

"Do you know why you are going, or are you just taking a ride on the train?"

[31]

"I know! Of course—I know why I'm going!" Eugene said angrily, confused. He stopped abruptly, bewildered, chastened. Ben continued to scowl at him. Then, quietly, with humility, Eugene said:

"No, Ben. I don't know why I'm going. Perhaps you're right. Perhaps I just want a ride on the train."

"When are you coming back, 'Gene?" said Ben.

"Why—at the end of the year, I think," Eugene answered.

"No," said Ben, "you're not."

"What do you mean, Ben?" Eugene said, troubled.

"You're not coming back, 'Gene," said Ben softly. "Do you know that?"

There was a pause.

"Yes," said Eugene, "I know it."

"Why aren't you coming back?" said Ben.

Eugene caught fiercely at the neckband of his shirt with a clawed hand.

"I want to go! Do you hear!" he cried.

"Yes," said Ben. "So did I. Why do you want to go?"

"There's nothing here for me," Eugene muttered.

"How long have you felt like this?" said Ben.

"Always," said Eugene. "As long as I can remember. But I didn't know about it until you—" He stopped.

"Until I what?" said Ben.

There was a pause.

"You are dead, Ben," Eugene muttered. "You must be dead. I saw you die, Ben." His voice rose sharply. "I tell you, I saw you die. Don't you remember? The front room upstairs that the dentist's wife has now?

Don't you remember, Ben? Coker, Helen, Bessie Gant who nursed you, Mrs. Pert? The oxygen tank? I tried to hold your hands together when they gave it to you." His voice rose to a scream. "Don't you remember? I tell you, you are dead, Ben."

"Fool," said Ben fiercely. "I am not dead."

There was a silence.

"Then," said Eugene very slowly, "which of us is the ghost, I wonder?"

Ben did not answer.

"Is this the Square, Ben? Is it you I'm talking to? Am I really here or not? And is this moonlight in the Square? Has all this happened?"

"How should I know?" said Ben again.

Within Gant's shop there was the ponderous tread of marble feet. Eugene leaped up and peered through the broad sheet of Jannadeau's dirty window. Upon his desk the strewn vitals of a watch winked with a thousand tiny points of bluish light. And beyond the jeweller's fenced space, where moonlight streamed into the ware-room through the tall side-window, the angels were walking to and fro like huge wound dolls of stone. The long cold pleats of their raiment rang with brittle clangor; their full decent breasts wagged in stony rhythms, and through the moonlight, with clashing wings the marble cherubim flew round and round. With cold ewe-bleatings the carved lambs grazed stiffly across the moon-drenched aisle.

"Do you see it?" cried Eugene. "Do you see it, Ben?"

[33]

"Yes," said Ben. "What about it? They have a right to, haven't they?"

"Not here! Not here!" said Eugene passionately. "It's not right, here! My God, this is the Square! There's the fountain! There's the City Hall! There's the Greek's lunch-room."

The bank-chimes struck the half hour.

"And there's the bank!" he cried.

"That makes no difference," said Ben.

"Yes," said Eugene, "it does!"

I am thy father's spirit, doomed for a certain term to walk the night——

"But not here! Not here, Ben!" said Eugene.

"Where?" said Ben wearily.

"In Babylon! In Thebes! In all the other places. But not here!" Eugene answered with growing passion. "There is a place where all things happen! But not here, Ben!"

My gods, with bird-cries in the sun, hang in the sky.

"Not here, Ben! It is not right!" Eugene said again.

The manifold gods of Babylon. Then, for a moment, Eugene stared at the dark figure on the rail, muttering in protest and disbelief: "Ghost! Ghost!"

"Fool," said Ben again, "I tell you I am not a ghost."

"Then, what are you?" said Eugene with strong excitement. "You are dead, Ben."

In a moment, more quietly, he added: "Or do men die?"

"How should I know?" said Ben.

"They say papa is dying. Did you know that, Ben?"
Eugene asked.

"Yes," said Ben.

"They have bought his shop. They are going to tear
it down and put up a skyscraper here."

"Yes," said Ben, "I know it."

We shall not come again. We never shall come back
again.

"Everything is going. Everything changes and passes
away. To-morrow I shall be gone and this—" he
stopped.

"This—what?" said Ben.

"This will be gone or— O God! Did all this happen?"
cried Eugene.

"How should I know, fool?" cried Ben angrily.

"What happens, Ben? What really happens?" said
Eugene. "Can you remember some of the same things
that I do? I have forgotten the old faces. Where are
they, Ben? What were their names? I forget the names
of people I knew for years. I get their faces mixed. I
get their heads stuck on other people's bodies. I think one
man has said what another said. And I forget—forget.
There is something I have lost and have forgotten. I
can't remember, Ben."

"What do you want to remember?" said Ben.

A stone, a leaf, an unfound door. And the forgotten
faces.

"I have forgotten names. I have forgotten faces. And
I remember little things," said Eugene. "I remember
the fly I swallowed on the peach, and the little boys on

tricycles at Saint Louis, and the mole on Grover's neck, and the Lackawanna freight-car, number 16356, on a siding near Gulfport. Once, in Norfolk, an Australian soldier on his way to France asked me the way to a ship; I remember that man's face."

He stared for an answer into the shadow of Ben's face, and then he turned his moon-bright eyes upon the Square.

And for a moment all the silver space was printed with the thousand forms of himself and Ben. There, by the corner in from Academy Street, Eugene watched his own approach; there, by the City Hall, he strode with lifted knees; there, by the curb upon the step, he stood, peopling the night with the great lost legion of himself —the thousand forms that came, that passed, that wove and shifted in unending change, and that remained unchanging Him.

And through the Square, unwoven from lost time, the fierce bright horde of Ben spun in and out its deathless loom. Ben, in a thousand moments, walked the Square: Ben of the lost years, the forgotten days, the unremembered hours; prowled by the moonlit façades; vanished, returned, left and rejoined himself, was one and many—deathless Ben in search of the lost dead lusts, the finished enterprise, the unfound door—unchanging Ben multiplying himself in form, by all the brick façades entering and coming out.

And as Eugene watched the army of himself and Ben, which were not ghosts, and which were lost, he saw himself—his son, his boy, his lost and virgin flesh—come

over past the fountain, leaning against the loaded can-
vas bag, and walking down with rapid crippled stride
past Gant's toward Niggerton in young pre-natal dawn.
And as he passed the porch where he sat watching, he
saw the lost child-face below the lumpy ragged cap,
drugged in the magic of unheard music, listening for the
far-forested horn-note, the speechless almost captured
pass-word. The fast boy-hands folded the fresh sheets,
but the fabulous lost face went by, steeped in its in-
cantations.

Eugene leaped to the railing.

"You! You! My son! My child! Come back! Come
back!"

His voice strangled in his throat: the boy had gone,
leaving the memory of his bewitched and listening face
turned to the hidden world. O lost!

And now the Square was thronging with their lost
bright shapes, and all the minutes of lost time collected
and stood still. Then, shot from them with projectile
speed, the Square shrank down the rails of destiny, and
was vanished with all things done, with all forgotten
shapes of himself and Ben.

And in his vision he saw the fabulous lost cities, buried
in the drifted silt of the earth—Thebes, the seven-gated,
and all the temples of the Daulian and Phocian lands,
and all Œnotria to the Tyrrhene gulf. Sunk in the
burial-urn of earth he saw the vanished cultures: the
strange sourceless glory of the Incas, the fragments of
lost epics upon a broken shard of Gnossic pottery, the
buried tombs of the Memphian kings, and imperial dust,

wound all about with gold and rotting linen, dead with their thousand bestial gods, their mute awakened *ushab-tii,* in their finished eternities.

He saw the billion living of the earth, the thousand billion dead: seas were withered, deserts flooded, mountains drowned; and gods and demons came out of the South, and ruled above the little rocket-flare of centuries, and sank—came to their Northern Lights of death, the muttering death-flared dusk of the completed gods.

But, amid the fumbling march of races to extinction, the giant rhythms of the earth remained. The seasons passed in their majestic processionals, and germinal Spring returned forever on the land—new crops, new men, new harvests, and new gods.

And then the voyages, the search for the happy land. In his moment of terrible vision he saw, in the tortuous ways of a thousand alien places, his foiled quest of himself. And his haunted face was possessed of that obscure and passionate hunger that had woven its shuttle across the seas, that had hung its weft among the Dutch in Pennsylvania, that had darkened his father's eyes to impalpable desire for wrought stone and the head of an angel. Hill-haunted, whose vision of the earth was mountain-walled, he saw the golden cities sicken in his eye, the opulent dark splendors turn to dingy gray. His brain was sick with the million books, his eyes with the million pictures, his body sickened on a hundred princely wines.

And rising from his vision, he cried: "I am not there

among the cities. I have sought down a million streets, until the goat-cry died within my throat, and I have found no city where I was, no door where I had entered, no place where I had stood."

Then, from the edges of moon-bright silence, Ben replied: "Fool, why do you look in the streets?"

Then Eugene said: "I have eaten and drunk the earth, I have been lost and beaten, and I will go no more."

"Fool," said Ben, "what do you want to find?"

"Myself, and an end to hunger, and the happy land," he answered. "For I believe in harbors at the end. O Ben, brother, and ghost, and stranger, you who could never speak, give me an answer now!"

Then, as he thought, Ben said: "There is no happy land. There is no end to hunger."

"And a stone, a leaf, a door? Ben?" Spoke, continued without speaking, to speak. "Who are, who never were, Ben, the seeming of my brain, as I of yours, my ghost, my stranger, who died, who never lived, as I? But if, lost seeming of my dreaming brain, you have what I have not—an answer?"

Silence spoke. ("I cannot speak of voyages. I belong here. I never got away," said Ben.)

"Then I of yours the seeming, Ben? Your flesh is dead and buried in these hills: my unimprisoned soul haunts through the million streets of life, living its spectral nightmare of hunger and desire. Where, Ben? Where is the world?"

"Nowhere," Ben said. "*You* are your world."

Inevitable catharsis by the threads of chaos. Unswerving punctuality of chance. Apexical summation, from the billion deaths of possibility, of things done.

"I shall save one land unvisited," said Eugene. *Et ego in Arcadia.*

And as he spoke, he saw that he had left the million bones of cities, the skein of streets. He was alone with Ben, and their feet were planted on darkness, their faces were lit with the cold high terror of the stars.

On the brink of the dark he stood, with only the dream of the cities, the million books, the spectral images of the people he had loved, who had loved him, whom he had known and lost. They will not come again. They never will come back again.

With his feet upon the cliff of darkness, he looked and saw the lights of no cities. It was, he thought, the strong good medicine of death.

"Is this the end?" he said. "Have I eaten life and have not found him? Then I will voyage no more."

"Fool," said Ben, *"this* is life. You have been nowhere."

"But in the cities?"

"There are none. There is one voyage, the first, the last, the only one."

"On coasts more strange than Cipango, in a place more far than Fez, I shall hunt him, the ghost and haunter of myself. I have lost the blood that fed me; I have died the hundred deaths that lead to life. By the slow thunder of the drums, the flare of dying cities, I have come to this dark place. And this is the true voyage, the good one, the best. And now prepare, my soul, for the beginning hunt. I will plumb seas stranger than those haunted by the Albatross."

He stood naked and alone in darkness, far from the lost world of the streets and faces; he stood upon the ramparts of his soul, before the lost land of himself; heard inland murmurs of lost seas, the far interior music of the horns. The last voyage, the longest, the best.

"O sudden and impalpable faun, lost in the thickets of myself, I will hunt you down until you cease to haunt my eyes with hunger. I heard your foot-falls in the desert, I saw your shadow in old buried cities, I heard your laughter running down a million streets, but I did not find you there. And no leaf hangs for me in the forest; I shall lift no stone upon the hills; I shall find no door in any city. But in the city of myself, upon the continent of my soul, I shall find the forgotten language, the lost world, a door where I may enter, and music strange as any ever sounded; I shall haunt you, ghost, along the labyrinthine ways until—until? O Ben, my ghost, an answer?"

But as he spoke, the phantom years scrolled up their vision, and only the eyes of Ben burned terribly in darkness, without an answer.

And day came, and the song of waking birds, and the Square, bathed in the young pearl light of morning. And a wind stirred lightly in the Square, and, as he looked, Ben, like a fume of smoke, was melted into dawn.

And the angels on Gant's porch were frozen in hard

marble silence, and at a distance life awoke, and there was a rattle of lean wheels, a slow clangor of shod hoofs. And he heard the whistle wail along the river.

Yet, as he stood for the last time by the angels of his father's porch, it seemed as if the Square already were far and lost; or, I should say, he was like a man who stands upon a hill above the town he has left, yet does not say "The town is near," but turns his eyes upon the distant soaring ranges.

Drunkenness

THE terrible draught smote him with the speed and power of a man's fist. He was made instantly drunken, and he knew instantly why men drank. It was, he knew, one of the great moments in his life—he lay, greedily watching the mastery of the grape over his virgin flesh, like a girl for the first time in the embrace of her lover. And suddenly, he knew how completely he was his father's son—how completely, and with what added power and exquisite refinement of sensation, was he Gantian. He exulted in the great length of his limbs and his body, through which the mighty liquor could better work its wizardry. In all the earth there was no other like him, no other fitted to be so sublimely and magnificently drunken. It was greater than all the music he had ever heard; it was as great as the highest poetry. Why had he never been told? Why had no one ever written adequately about it? Why, when it was possible to buy a god in a bottle, and drink him off, and become a god oneself, were men not forever drunken?

He had a moment of great wonder—the magnificent wonder with which we discover the simple and unspeakable things that lie buried and known, but unconfessed, in us. So might a man feel if he wakened after death and found himself in Heaven.

Then a divine paralysis crept through his flesh. His limbs were numb; his tongue thickened until he could not bend it to the cunning sounds of words. He spoke aloud, repeating difficult phrases over and over, filled with wild laughter and delight at his effort. Behind his drunken body his brain hung poised like a falcon, looking on him with scorn, with tenderness, looking on all laughter with grief and pity. There lay in him something that could not be seen and could not be touched, which was above and beyond him—an eye within an eye, a brain above a brain, the Stranger that dwelt in him and regarded him and was him, and that he did not know. But, thought he, I am alone now in this house; if I can come to know him, I will.

He got up, and reeled out of the alien presences of light and warmth in the kitchen; he went out into the hall where a dim light burned and the high walls gave back their grave-damp chill. This, he thought, is the house.

He sat down upon the hard mission settle, and listened to the cold drip of silence. This is the house in which I have been an exile. There is a stranger in the house, and there's a stranger in me.

O house of Admetus, in whom (although I was a god) I have endured so many things. Now, house, I am not afraid. No ghost need fear come by me. If there's a door in silence, let it open. My silence can be greater than your own. And you who are in me, and who I am, come forth beyond this quiet shell of flesh that makes no posture to deny you. There is none to look at us: O come, my brother and my lord, with unbent face. If I had 40,000 years, I should give all but the ninety last to silence. I should grow to the earth like a hill or a rock. Unweave the fabric of nights and days; unwind my life back to my birth; subtract me into nakedness again, and build me back with all the sums I have not counted. Or let me look upon the living face of darkness; let me hear the terrible sentence of your voice.

There was nothing but the living silence of the house: no doors were opened.

April Night and Morning

THE plum-tree, black and brittle, rocks stiffly in winter wind. Her million little twigs are frozen in spears of ice. But in the Spring, lithe and heavy, she will bend under her great load of fruit and blossoms. She will grow young again. Red plums will ripen, will be shaken desperately upon the tiny stems. They will fall bursted on the loamy wet earth; when the wind blows in the orchard the air will be filled with dropping plums; the night will be filled with the sound of their dropping, and a great tree of birds will sing, burgeoning, blossoming richly, filling the air also with warm-throated plum-dropping bird-notes.

The harsh hill-earth has moistly thawed and softened, rich soaking rain falls, fresh-bladed tender grass like soft hair growing sparsely streaks the land.

My Brother Ben's face, thought Eugene, is like a piece of slightly yellow ivory; his high white head is knotted fiercely by his old man's scowl; his mouth is like a knife, his smile the flicker of light across a blade. His face is like a blade, and a knife, and a flicker of light: it is delicate and fierce, and scowls beautifully forever, and when he fastens his hard white fingers and his scowling eyes upon a thing he wants to fix, he sniffs with sharp and private concentration through his long pointed nose. Thus women, looking, feel a well of tenderness for his pointed, bumpy, always scowling face: his hair shines like that of a young boy—it is crinkled and crisp as lettuce.

Into the April night-and-morning streets goes Ben. The night is brightly pricked with cool and tender stars. The orchard stirs leafily in the short fresh wind. Ben prowls softly out of the sleeping house. His thin bright face is dark within the orchard. There is a smell of nicotine and shoe leather under the young blossoms. His pigeon-toed tan shoes ring musically up the empty streets. Lazily slaps the water in the fountain on the Square; all the firemen are asleep—but Big Bill Merrick, the brave cop, hog-jowled and red, leans swinishly over mince-pie and coffee in Uneeda Lunch. The warm good ink-smell beats in rich waves into the street: a whistling train howls off into the Springtime South.

By the cool orchards in the dark the paper-carriers go. The copper legs of negresses in their dark dens stir. The creek brawls cleanly.

Euripides in the Wilderness

E READ a great deal—but at random, for pleasure. He read Defoe, Smollet, Sterne, and Fielding—the fine salt of the English novel lost, during the reign of the Widow of Windsor, beneath an ocean of tea and molasses. He read the tales of Boccaccio, and all that remained of a tattered copy of the *Heptameron*. At Buck Benson's suggestion, he read Murray's *Euripides* (at the time he was reading the Greek text of the *Alcestis*—noblest and loveliest of all the myths of Love and Death). He saw the grandeur of the *Prometheus* fable—but the fable moved him more than the play of Æschylus. In fact, Æschylus he found sublime—and dull: he could not understand his great reputation. Rather—he could. He was Literature—a

writer of masterpieces. He was almost as great a bore
as Cicero—that windy old moralist who came out so
boldly in favor of Old Age and Friendship. Sophocles
was an imperial poet—he spoke like God among flashes
of lightning: the *Œdipus Rex* is not only one of the
greatest plays in the world, it is one of the greatest
stories. This story—perfect, inevitable, and fabulous—
wreaked upon him the nightmare coincidence of Destiny. It held him birdlike before its great snake-eye of
wisdom and horror. And Euripides (whatever the dis-
paragement of pedantry) he thought one of the greatest
lyrical singers in all poetry.

He liked all weird fable and wild invention, in prose or
verse, from the *Golden Ass* to Samuel Taylor Coleridge,
the chief prince of the moon and magic. But he liked
the fabulous wherever he found it, and for whatever
purpose.

The best fabulists have often been the greatest satir-
ists: satire (as with Aristophanes, Voltaire, and Swift)
is a high and subtle art, quite beyond the barnyard
snipings and wholesale geese-slaughterings of the present degenerate age. Great satire needs the sustenance of
great fable. Swift's power of invention is incomparable:
there's no better fabulist in the world.

He read Poe's stories, *Frankenstein,* and the plays of
Lord Dunsany. He read *Sir Gawayne and the Grene
Knight* and the *Book of Tobit.* He did not want his
ghosts and marvels explained. Magic was magic. He
wanted old ghosts—not Indian ghosts, but ghosts in
armor, the spirits of old kings, and pillioned ladies with

high coned hats. Then, for the first time, he thought of the lonely earth he dwelt on. Suddenly, it was strange to him that he should read *Euripides* there in the wilderness.

Around him lay the village; beyond, the ugly rolling land, sparse with cheap farmhouses; beyond all this, America—more land, more wooden houses, more towns, hard and raw and ugly. He was reading Euripides, and all around him a world of white and black was eating fried food. He was reading of ancient sorceries and old ghosts, but did an old ghost ever come to haunt this land? The ghost of Hamlet's Father, in Connecticut,

> ". . . . . . I am thy father's spirit,
> Doomed for a certain term to walk the night
> Between Bloomington and Portland, Maine."

He felt suddenly the devastating impermanence of the nation. Only the earth endured—the gigantic American earth, bearing upon its awful breast a world of flimsy rickets. Only the earth endured—this broad terrific earth that had no ghosts to haunt it. Stogged in the desert, half-broken and overthrown, among the columns of lost temples strewn, there was no ruined image of Menkaura, there was no alabaster head of Akhnaton. Nothing had been done in stone. Only this earth endured, upon whose lonely breast he read Euripides. Within its hills he had been held a prisoner; upon its plain he walked, alone, a stranger.

O Young Love, Return

COME up into the hills, O my young love. Return! O lost, and by the wind grieved, ghost, come back again, as first I knew you in the timeless valley, where we shall feel ourselves anew, bedded on magic in the month of June. There was a place where all the sun went glistering in your hair, and from the hill we could have put a finger on a star. Where is the day that melted into one rich noise? Where the music of your flesh, the rhyme of your teeth, the dainty languor of your legs, your small firm arms, your slender fingers, to be bitten like an apple, and the little cherry-teats of your white breasts? And where are all the tiny wires of finespun maidenhair? Quick are the mouths of earth, and quick the teeth that fed upon this loveliness. You who were made for music, will hear music no more: in your dark house the winds are silent. Ghost, ghost, come back from that marriage that we did not foresee, return not into life, but into magic, where we have never died, into the enchanted wood, where we still lie, strewn on the grass. Come up into the hills, O my young love: return. O lost, and by the wind grieved, ghost, come back again.

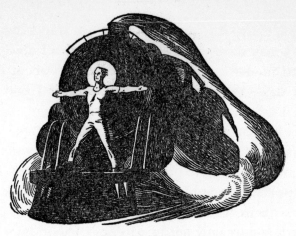

Departure

THE marvellous hills were blooming in the dusk. Eliza pursed her lips reflectively a moment, then continued:

"Well, when you get way up there—as the feller says—in Yankee-dom, you want to look up your Uncle Emerson and all your Boston kin. Your Aunt Lucy took a great liking to you when they were down here—they always said they'd be glad to see any of us if we ever came up—when you're a stranger in a strange land it's mighty good sometimes to have some one you know. And say—when you see your Uncle Emerson, you might just tell him not to be surprised to see me at any time now" (She nodded pertly at him)—"I reckon I can pick right up and light out the same as the next fellow when I get ready—I may just pack up and come—without saying a word to any one—I'm not going to spend all my days slaving away in the kitchen

—it don't pay—if I can turn a couple of trades here this Fall, I may start out to see the world like I always intended to—I was talking to Cash Rankin about it the other day—'Why, Mrs. Gant,' he said, 'if I had your head I'd be a rich man in five years—you're the best trader in this town,' he said. 'Don't you talk to me about any more trades,' I said—'when I get rid of what I've got now I'm going to get out of it, and not even listen to any one who says real-estate to me—we can't take any of it with us, Cash,' I said—'there are no pockets in shrouds and we only need six feet of earth to bury us in the end—so I'm going to pull out and begin to enjoy life—as the feller says—before it's too late'—'Well, I don't know that I blame you, Mrs. Gant,' he said—'I reckon you're right—we can't take any of it with us,' he said—'and besides, even if we could, what good would it do us where we're goin'?'—Now here" (she addressed Eugene with sudden change, with the old loose masculine gesture of her hand)—"here's the thing I'm going to do—you know that lot I told you I owned on Sunset Crescent——"

And now the terrible silence came between them once again.

The marvellous hills were blooming in the dusk. We shall not come again. We never shall come back again.

Without speech now they faced each other, without speech they knew each other. In a moment Eliza turned quickly from him and with the queer unsteady steps with which she had gone out from the room where Ben lay dying, she moved toward the door.

[53]

He rushed back across the walk and with a single bound took the steps that mounted to the porch. He caught the rough hands that she held clasped across her body, and drew them swiftly, fiercely, to his breast.

"Good-bye," he muttered harshly. "Good-bye! Good-bye, mama!" A wild, strange cry, like that of a beast in pain, was torn from his throat. His eyes were blind with tears; he tried to speak, to get into a word, a phrase, all the pain, the beauty, and the wonder of their lives—every step of that terrible voyage which his incredible memory and intuition took back to the dwelling of her womb. But no word came, no word could come; he kept crying hoarsely again and again, "Good-bye, good-bye."

She understood, she knew all he felt and wanted to say, her small weak eyes were wet as his with tears, her face was twisted in the painful grimace of sorrow, and she kept saying:

"Poor child! Poor child! Poor child!" Then she whispered huskily, faintly: "We must try to love one another."

The terrible and beautiful sentence, the last, the final wisdom that the earth can give, is remembered at the end, is spoken too late, wearily. It stands there, awful and untraduced, above the dusty racket of our lives. No forgetting, no forgiving, no denying, no explaining, no hating.

O mortal and perishing love, born with this flesh and dying with this brain, your memory will haunt the earth forever.

[54]

Journey to the North

So HERE they are now, three atoms on the huge breast of the indifferent earth, three youths out of a little town walled far away within the great rim of the silent mountains, already a distant, lonely dot upon the immense and sleeping visage of the continent. Here they are—three youths bound for the first time towards their image of the distant and enchanted city, sure that even though so many of their comrades had found there only dust and bitterness, the shining victory will be theirs. Here they are hurled onward in the great projectile of the train across the lonely visage of the everlasting earth. Here they are—three nameless grains of life among the man-swarm ciphers of the earth, three faces of the million faces, three drops in the unceasing flood—and each of them a flame, a light, a glory, sure that his destiny is written in the blazing stars, his life shone over by the fortunate watches of the moon, his fame nourished and sustained by the huge earth, whose single darling charge he is, on whose immortal stillness he is flung onward in the night, his glorious fate set in the very brain and forehead of the fabulous, the unceasing city, of whose million-footed life he will tomorrow be a part.

Therefore they stand upon the rocking platform of the train, wild and dark and jubilant from the fierce liquor they have drunk, but more wild and dark and jubilant from the fury swelling in their hearts, the mad fury pounding in their veins, the savage, exultant and unutterable fury working like a madness in the adyts of their soul. And the great wheels smash and pound beneath their feet, the great wheels pound and smash and give a rhyme to madness, a tongue to hunger and desire, a certitude to all the savage, drunken, and exultant fury that keeps mounting, rising, swelling in them all the time!

Click, clack, clackety-clack; click, clack, clackety-
clack; click, clack, clackety-clack; clackety-clackety-
clack!

Hip, hop, hackety-hack; stip, step, rackety-rack;
come and fetch it, come and fetch it, hickety hickety
hack!

Rock, reel, smash, and swerve; hit it, hit it, on the
curve; steady, steady, does the trick, keep her steady as
a stick; eat the earth, eat the earth, slam and slug and
beat the earth, and let her whir-r, and let her pur-r, at
eighty per-r!

—Whew-w!

—Wow!

—God-dam!

—Put 'er there, boy!

—Put 'er there—whah!—*whah-h!* you ole long-legged
frowsle-headed son-of-a-bitch!

—Whoop-ee! Whah—*whah-h!* Why, Go-d-d-dam!

—Whee! Vealer rog?

—Wadja say? Gant hearya!

—I say 'ja vealer rog? Wow! Pour it to her, son! Give
'er the gas! We're out to see the world! Run her off
the god-damn track, boy! We don't need no rail, do we?

—Hell no! Which way does this damn train go, any-
way, after it leaves Virginia?

—Maryland.

—Maryland my—! I don't want to go to Maryland!
To hell with Mary's land! Also to hell with Mary's lamb
and Mary's calf and Mary's blue silk underdrawers!
Good old Lucy's the girl for me—the loosier the better!

[57]

Give me Lucy any day! Good old Lucy Bowles, God bless her—she's the pick of the crowd, boys! Here's to Lucy!

Robert! Art there, boy?

—Aye, aye, sir! Present!

—Hast seen the damsel down in Lower Seven?

—I' sooth, sir, that I have! A comely wench, I trow!

—Peace, fool! Don't think, proud Princocke, thou canst snare this dove of innocence into the nets of infamous desire with stale reversions of thy wit! Out, out, vile lendings! An' but thou carried'st at thy shrunken waist that monstrous tun of guts thou takest for a brain 'twould so beslubber this receiving earth with lard as was not seen twixt here and Nottingham since butter shrove! Out, out upon you, scrappings of the pot! A dove, a doe, it is a faultless swan, I say, a pretty thing!

Now Virginia lay dreaming in the moonlight. In Louisiana bayous the broken moonlight shivers the broken moonlight quivers the light of many rivers lay dreaming in the moonlight beaming in the moonlight dreaming in the moonlight moonlight moonlight seeming in the moonlight moonlight moonlight to be gleaming to be streaming in the moonlight moonlight moonlight moonlight moonlight moonlight moonlight moonlight

—Mo-hoo-oonlight-oonlight oonlight oonlight oonlight oonlight oonlight oonlight oonlight oonlight

—To be seeming to be dreaming in the moonlight!

WHAM!

SMASH!

—Now! God-dam, let her have it! Wow-w!

With slamming roar, hoarse waugh, and thunder-bolted light, the southbound train is gone in one projec-tile smash of wind-like fury, and the open empty silence of its passing fills us, thrills us, stills us with the vision of Virginia in the moonlight, with the dream-still magic of Virginia in the moon.

And now, as if with recollected force, the train gains power from the train it passed, leaps, gathers, springs beneath them, smashes on with recollected demon's fury in the dark . . .

With slam-bang of devil's racket and God-dam of curse—give us the bottle, drink, boys, drink!—the power of Virginia lies compacted in the moon. To you, God-dam of devil's magic and slam-bang of drive, fire-flame of the terrific furnace, slam of rod, storm-stroke of pis-toned wheel and thunderbolt of speed, great earth-devourer, city-bringer—hail!

To you, also, old glint of demon hawkeyes on the rail and the dark gloved hand of cunning—you, there, old bristle-crops!—Tom Wilson, H. F. Cline, or T. J. John-son—whatever the hell your name is——

CASEY JONES! Open the throttle, boy, and let her rip! Boys, I'm a belly-busting bastard from the State of old Catawba—rootin' tootin' shootin' son-of-a-bitch from Saw Tooth Gap in Buncombe—why, God help this lovely bastard of a train—it is the best damned train that ever turned a wheel since Casey Jones's father was a pup—why, you sweet bastard, run! Eat up Virginia!—Give her the throttle, you old goggle-eyed son-of-a-bitch up there!—Pour it to her! Let 'er have it, you nigger-Baptist bastard of a shovelling fireman—let 'er rip!—Wow! By God, we'll be in Washington for breakfast!

—Why, God bless this lovely bastard of a train! It is the best damned train that ever pulled a car since Grant took Richmond!—Which way does the damn thing go? —Pennsylvania?—Well, that's all right! Don't you say a word against Pennsylvania! My father came from Pennsylvania, boys, he was the best damned man that ever lived—He was a stonecutter and he's better than any son-of-a-bitch of a plumber you ever saw—He's got a cancer and six doctors and they can't kill him!—But to hell with going where we go!—We're out to see the world, boy!—To hell with Baltimore, New York, Boston! Run her off the God-damn rails! We're going West! Run her through the woods—cross fields—rivers, through the hills! Hell's pecker! But I'll shove her up the grade and through the gap, no double-header needed!—Let's see the world now! Through Nebraska, boy! Let's shove her through, now, you can do it!—Let's run her through Ohio, Kansas, and the unknown plains! Come on, you hogger, let's see the great plains and the fields of wheat —Stop off in Dakota, Minnesota, and the fertile places— Give us a minute while you breathe to put our foot upon it, to feel it spring back with the deep elastic feeling, 8000 miles below, unrolled and lavish, depthless, different from the East.

Now Virgina lay dreaming in the moonlight! And on Florida's bright waters the fair and lovely daughters of the Wilsons and the Potters; the Cabots and the Lowells; the Weisbergs and O'Hares; the Astors and the Goulds; the Ransoms and the Rands; the Westalls and the Pattons and the Webbs; the Reynolds and McRaes; the Spanglers and the Beams; the Gudgers and the Blakes; the Pedersons and Craigs—all the lovely daughters, the Robinsons and Waters, the millionaires' sweet daughters, the Boston maids, the Beacon Slades, the Back Bay Wades, all of the merchant, lawyer, railroad and well-monied grades of Hudson River daughters in the moon's bright living waters—lay dreaming in the moonlight, beaming in the moonlight, seeming in the moonlight, to be dreaming to be gleaming in the moon.

—Give 'em hell, son!

—Here, give him another drink!—Attaboy! Drink her down!

—Drink her down—drink her down—drink her down —damn your soul—drink her down!

—By God, I'll drink her down and flood the whole end of Virginia, I'll drown out Maryland, make a flood in Pennsylvania—I tell you boys I'll float 'em, I'll raise 'em up, I'll bring 'em down stream, now—I mean the Potters and the Waters, the rich men's lovely daughters, the city's tender daughters, the Hudson River daughters——

Lay dreaming in the moonlight, beaming in the moonlight, to be seeming to be beaming in the moonlight moonlight moonlight oonlight oonlight oonlight oonlight oonlight.

And Virginia lay dreaming in the moon.

Then the moon blazed down upon the vast desolation of the American coasts, and on all the glut and hiss of tides, on all the surge and foaming slide of waters on lone beaches. The moon blazed down on 18,000 miles of coast, on the million sucks and scoops and hollows of the shore, and on the great wink of the sea, that ate the earth minutely and eternally. The moon blazed down upon the wilderness, it fell on sleeping woods, it dripped through moving leaves, it swarmed in weaving patterns on the earth, and it filled the cat's still eye with blazing yellow. The moon slept over mountains and lay in silence in the desert, and it carved the shadows of great rocks like time. The moon was mixed with flowing rivers, and it was buried in the heart of lakes, and it trembled on the water like bright fish. The moon steeped all the earth in its living and unearthly substance, it had a thousand visages, it painted continental space with ghostly light; and its light was proper to the nature of all the things it touched: it came in with the sea, it flowed with the rivers, and it was still and living on clear spaces in the forest where no men watched.

And in woodland darkness great birds fluttered to their sleep—in sleeping woodlands strange and secret birds, the teal, the nightjar, and the flying rail went to their sleep with flutterings dark as hearts of sleeping men. In fronded beds and on the leaves of unfamiliar

plants where the tarantula, the adder, and the asp had
fed themselves asleep on their own poisons, and on lush
jungle depths where green-golden, bitter red and glossy
blue proud tufted birds cried out with brainless scream,
the moonlight slept.

The moonlight slept above dark herds moving with
slow grazings in the night, it covered lonely little vil-
lages; but most of all it fell upon the unbroken undula-
tion of the wilderness, and it blazed on windows, and
moved across the face of sleeping men.

Sleep lay upon the wilderness, it lay across the faces
of the nations, it lay like silence on the hearts of sleeping
men; and low upon lowlands, and high upon hills,
flowed gently sleep, smooth-sliding sleep—sleep—sleep.

—Robert——
—Go on to bed, Gene, go to bed now, go to bed.
—There's shump'n I mush shay t'you——
—Damn fool! Go to bed!
—Go to bed, my balls! I'll go to bed when I'm God-
damn good and ready! I'll not go to bed when there's
shump'n I mush shay t'you——
—Go on to bed now, Gene. You've had enough.
—Creasman, you're a good fellow maybe but I don't
know you. . . . You keep out of this. . . . Robert
. . . I'm gonna tell y' shump'n. . . . You made a re-
mark t'night I didn' like—Prayin' for me, are they,
Robert?
—You damn fool!—You don't know what you're
talkin' 'bout! Go on to bed!——

—I'll go to bed, you bastard—I got shump'n to shay t'you!—Prayin' for me, are yuh?—Pray for yourself, y' bloody little Deke!

—Damn fool's crazy! Go on to bed now——

—I'll bed yuh, you son-of-a-bitch! What was it y' said that day?——

—What day? You damned fool, you don't know what you're saying!

—I'll tell yuh what day!—Coming along Chestnut Street that day after school with you and me and Sunny Jim Curtis and Ed Petrie and Bob Pegram and Carl Hartshorn and Monk Paul—and the rest of those boys——

—You damn fool! Chestnut Street! I don't know what you're talking about!

—Yes, you do!—You and me and Bob and Carl and Irwin and Jim Homes and some other boys—'Member what y' said, yuh son-of-a-bitch? Old man English was in his yard there burning up some leaves and it was October and we were comin' along there after school and you could smell the leaves and it was after school and you said, "Here's Mr. Gant the tombstone cutter's son."

—You damn fool! I don't know what you're talking about!——

—Yes, you do, you cheap Deke son-of-a-bitch—Too good to talk to us on the street when you were sucking around after Bruce Martin or Steve Patton or Jack Marriott—but a life-long brother—oh! couldn't see enough of us, could you, when you were alone?

[64]

—The damn fool's crazy!

—Crazy, am I?—Well, we never had any old gummy grannies tied down and hidden in the attic—which is more than some people that I know can say!—you son-of-a-bitch—who do you think you are with your big airs and big Deke pin!—My people were better people than your crowd ever hoped to be—we've been here longer and we're better people—and as for the tombstone cutter's son, my father was the best damned stonecutter that ever lived—he's dying of cancer and all the doctors in the world can't kill him—he's a better man than any little ex-police court magistrate who calls himself a judge will ever be—and that goes for you too—you——

Why, you crazy fool! I never said anything about your father——

To hell with you, you damn little bootlicking——

Come on Gene come on you've had enough you're drunk now come on.

Why God-damn you to hell, I hate your guts you——

All right, all right—He's drunk! He's crazy—Come on, Bill! Leave him alone!—He don't know what he's doing——

All right. Good night, Gene. . . . Be careful now—see you in the morning, boy.

All right, Robert, I mean nothing against you—you——

All right!—All right!—Come on, Bill. Let him alone! Good night, Gene—Come on—let's go to bed!——

To bed to bed to bed to bed to bed! So, so, so, so, so!

Make no noise, make no noise, draw the curtains; so, so, so. We'll go to supper i' the morning: so so, so.

And Ile goe to bedde at noone.

Alone, alone now, down the dark, the green, the jungle aisle between the dark drugged snorings of the sleepers. The pause, the stir, the sigh, the sudden shift, the train that now rumbles on through the dark forests of the dream-charged moon-enchanted mind its monotone of silence and forever: Out of these prison bands of clothes, now, rip, tear, toss, and haul while the green-curtained sleepers move from jungle depths and the even-pounding silence of eternity—into the stiff white sheets, the close, hot air, his long body crookedly athwart, lights out, to see it shining faintly in the coffined undersurface of the berth above—and sleepless, Virginia floating, dreamlike, in the still white haunting of the moon——

—At night, great trains will pass us in the timeless spell of an unsleeping hypnosis, an endless, and unfathomable stupefaction. Then suddenly in the unwaking never sleeping century of the night, the sensual limbs of carnal whited nakedness that stir with drowsy silken warmth in the green secrecies of Lower Seven, the slow swelling and lonely and swarmhaunted land—and suddenly, suddenly, silence and thick hardening lust of dark exultant joy, the dreamlike passage of Virginia!— Then in the watches of the night a pause, the sudden silence of up-welling night, and unseen faces, voices, laughter, and farewells upon a lonely little night-time

station—the lost and lonely voices of Americans:—
"Good-bye! Good-bye, now! Write us when you get
there, Helen! Tell Bob he's got to write!—Give my love
to Emily!—Good-bye, good-bye now—write us, soon!"—
And then the secret, silken and subdued rustling past
the thick green curtains and the sleepers, the low re-
spectful negroid tones of the black porter—and then the
whistle cry, the tolling bell, the great train mounting to
its classic monotone again, and presently the last lights
of a little town, the floating void and loneliness of moon-
haunted earth—Virginia!

Also, in the dream—thickets of eternal night—there
will be huge steamings on the rail, the sudden smash,
the wall of light, the sudden flarings of wild, roaring light
upon the moon-haunted and dream-tortured faces of
the sleepers!

—And finally, in that dark jungle of the night, through
all the visions, memories, and enchanted weavings of
the timeless and eternal spell of time, the moment of
forever—there are two horsemen, riding, riding, riding
in the night.

Who are they? Oh, we know them with our life and
they will ride across the land, the moon-haunted passage
of our lives forever. Their names are Death and Pity,
and we know their face: our brother and our father
ride ever beside us in the dream-enchanted spell and
vista of the night; the hooves keep level time beside the
rhythms of the train.

Horsed on the black and moon-maned steeds of fury,
cloaked in the dark of night, the spell of time, dream-

pale, eternal, they are rushing on across the haunted land, the moon-enchanted wilderness, and their hooves make level thunder with the train.

Pale Pity and Lean Death their names are, and they will ride forevermore the moon-plantations of Virginia keeping time time time to the level thunder of the train pounding time time time as with four-hooved thunder of phantasmal hooves they pound forever level with the train across the moon-plantations of Virginia.

Quadrupedante putrem sonitu quatit ungula campum as with storm-phantasmal hooves Lean Death and Pale Pity with quadrupedante putrem sonitu quatit ungula campum . . . campum . . . quadrupedante . . . putrem . . . putrem . . . putrem putrem putrem as with sonitu quatit ungula campum quadrupedante putrem . . . putrem . . . putrem putrem putrem . . . putrem . . . putrem . . . putrem putrem putrem quadrupedante quadrupedante quadrupedante putrem putrem as with sonitu quatit ungula campum quadrupedante putrem . . . putrem . . . putrem putrem putrem . . . as with sonitu quatit ungula campum quadrupedante putrem . . . ungula campum . . . campum . . . ungula . . . ungula campum . . .

At day-break suddenly, he awoke. The first light of the day, faint, gray-white, shone through the windows of his berth. The faint gray light fell on the stiff white linen, feverishly scuffed and rumpled in the distressful visions of the night, on the hot pillows and on the long cramped figure of the boy, where dim reflection already could be seen on the polished surface of the berth above his head. Outside, that smoke-gray light had stolen almost imperceptibly through the darkness. The air now shone gray-blue and faintly luminous with day, and the old brown earth was just beginning to emerge in that faint light. Slowly, the old brown earth was coming from the darkness with that strange and awful stillness which the first light of the day has always brought.

The earth emerged with all its ancient and eternal quality: stately and solemn and lonely-looking in that first light, it filled men's hearts with all its ancient wonder. It seemed to have been there forever, and, though they had never seen it before, to be more familiar to them than their mother's face. And at the same time it seemed they had discovered it once more, and if they had been the first men who ever saw the earth, the solemn joy of this discovery could not have seemed more strange or more familiar. Seeing it, they felt nothing but silence and wonder in their hearts, and were naked and alone and stripped down to their bare selves, as near to truth as men can ever come. They knew that they would die and that the earth would last forever. And with that feeling of joy, wonder, and sorrow in their hearts, they knew that another day had gone, another day had come, and they knew how brief and lonely are man's days.

The old earth went floating past them in that first gaunt light of the morning, and it seemed to be the face of time itself, and the noise the train made was the noise of silence. They were fixed there in that classic design of time and silence. The engine smoke went striding out upon the air, the old earth—field and wood and hill and stream and wood and field and hill—went stroking, floating past with a kind of everlasting repetitiveness, and the train kept making on its steady noise that was like silence and forever—until it almost seemed that they were poised there in that image of eternity forever—in moveless movement, unsilent silence, spaceless flight.

All of the noises, rhythms, sounds and variations of the train seemed to belong to all the visions, images, wild cries and oaths and songs and haunting memories of the night before, and now the train itself seemed united to this infinite monotone of silence, and the boy felt that this land now possessed his life, that he had known it forever, and could now think only with a feeling of unbelief and wonder that yesterday—just yesterday—he had left his home in the far mountains and now was stroking eastward, northward towards the sea.

And against the borders of the East, pure, radiant, for the first time seen in the unbelievable wonder of its new discovery, bringing to all of us, as it had always done, the first life that was ever known on this earth, the golden banner of the day appeared.

O Lost

. . . a stone, a leaf, an unfound door; of a stone, a leaf, a door. And of all the forgotten faces.

Naked and alone we came into exile. In her dark womb we did not know our mother's face; from the prison of her flesh have we come into the unspeakable and incommunicable prison of this earth.

Which of us has known his brother? Which of us has looked into his father's heart? Which of us has not remained forever prison-pent? Which of us is not forever a stranger and alone?

O waste of loss, in the hot mazes, lost, among bright stars on this most weary unbright cinder, lost! Remembering speechlessly we seek the great forgotten language, the lost lane-end into heaven, a stone, a leaf, an unfound door. Where? When?

O lost, and by the wind grieved, ghost, come back again.

Who Has Known Fury?

WHO has seen fury riding in the mountains?
Who has known fury striding in the
storm? Who has been mad with fury in his
youth, given no rest or peace or certitude
by fury, driven on across the earth by fury, until the
great vine of the heart was broke, the sinews wrenched,
the little tenement of bone, blood, marrow, brain, and
feeling in which great fury raged, was twisted, wrung,
depleted, worn out, and exhausted by the fury which it
could not lose or put away? Who has known fury, how
it came?

How have we breathed him, drunk him, eaten fury
to the core, until we have him in us now and cannot lose
him anywhere we go? It is a strange and subtle worm
that will be forever feeding at our heart. It is a madness

working in our brain, a hunger growing from the food it feeds upon, a devil moving in the conduits of our blood, it is a spirit wild and dark and uncontrollable forever swelling in our soul, and it is in the saddle now, horsed upon our lives, rowelling the spurs of its insatiate desire into our naked and defenseless sides, our owner, master, and the mad and cruel tyrant who goads us on forever down the blind and brutal tunnel of kaleidoscopic days at the end of which is nothing but the blind mouth of the pit and darkness and no more.

Then, then, will fury leave us, he will cease from those red channels of our life he has so often run, another sort of worm will work at that great vine, whereat he fed. Then, then, indeed, he must give over, fold his camp, retreat; there is no place for madness in a dead man's brain, no place for hunger in a dead man's flesh, and in a dead man's heart there is a place for no desire.

At what place of velvet-breasted night long long ago, and in what leafy darkened street of mountain summer, hearing the footsteps of approaching lovers in the night, the man's voice, low, hushed, casual, confiding, suddenly the low rich welling of a woman's laughter, tender and sensual in the dark, going, receding, fading, and then the million-noted silence of the night again? In what ancient light of fading day in a late summer; what wordless passion then of sorrow, joy, and ecstasy—was he betrayed to fury when it came?

Or in the black dark of some forgotten winter's morning, child of the storm and brother to the dark, alone and wild and secret in the night as he leaned down

against the wind's strong wall towards Niggertown,
blocking his folded papers as he went, and shooting
them terrifically in the wind's wild blast against the
shack-walls of the jungle-sleeping blacks, himself alone
awake, wild, secret, free and stormy as the wild wind's
blast, giving it howl for howl and yell for yell, with
madness, and a demon's savage and exultant joy, up-
welling in his throat! Oh, was he then, on such a night,
betrayed to fury—was it then, on such a night, that fury
came?

He never knew; it may have been a rock, a stone,
a leaf, the moths of golden light as warm and moving
in a place of magic green, it may have been the storm-
wind howling in the barren trees, the ancient fading
light of day in some forgotten summer, the huge un-
folding mystery of undulant, on-coming night.

Oh, it might have been all this in the April and most
lilac darkness of some forgotten morning as he saw
the clean line of the East cleave into morning at the
mountain's ridge. It may have been the first light, bird-
song, an end to labor and the sweet ache and pure
fatigue of the lightened shoulder as he came home at
morning hearing the single lonely hoof, the jinking
bottles, and the wheel upon the street again, and smelled
the early morning breakfast smells, the smoking wheat-
cakes, and the pungent sausages, the steaks, biscuits,
grits, and fried green apples, and the brains and eggs.
It may have been the coil of pungent smoke upcurling
from his father's chimney, the clean sweet gardens and
the peach-bloom, apples, crinkled lettuce wet with dew,

bloom and cherry bloom down drifting in their magic snow within his father's orchard, and his father's giant figure awake now and astir, and moving in his house!

Oh, ever to wake at morning knowing he was there! To feel the fire-full chimney-throat roar up a-tremble with the blast of his terrific fires, to hear the first fire crackling in the kitchen range, to hear the sounds of morning in the house, the smells of breakfast and the feeling of security never to be changed! Oh, to hear him prowling like a wakened lion below, the stertorous hoarse frenzy of his furious breath; to hear the ominous muttering mounting to faint howls as with infuriated relish he prepared the roaring invective of the morning's tirade, to hear him muttering as the coal went rattling out upon the fire, to hear him growling as savagely the flame shot up the trembling chimney-throat, to hear him muttering back and forth now like a raging beast, finally to hear his giant stride racing through the house prepared now, storming to the charge, and the well-remembered howl of his awakened fury as springing to the door-way of the back-room stairs he flung it open, yelling at them to awake.

Was it in such a way, one time as he awoke, and heard below his father's lion-ramp of morning that fury came? He never knew, no more than one could weave the great web of his life back through the brutal chaos of ten thousand furious days, unwind the great vexed pattern of his life to silence, peace, and certitude in the magic land of new beginnings, no return.

Man's Youth

MAN'S youth is a wonderful thing: it is so full
of anguish and of magic and he never
comes to know it as it is, until it has gone
from him forever. It is the thing he cannot
bear to lose, it is the thing whose passing he watches
with infinite sorrow and regret, it is the thing whose loss
he must lament forever, and it is the thing whose loss
he really welcomes with a sad and secret joy, the thing
he would never willingly re-live again, could it be
restored to him by any magic.

Why is this? The reason is that the strange and bitter
miracle of life is nowhere else so evident as in our youth.
And what is the essence of that strange and bitter miracle of life which we feel so poignantly, so unutterably,
with such a bitter pain and joy, when we are young?
It is this: that being rich, we are so poor; that being
mighty, we can yet have nothing; that seeing, breathing,
smelling, tasting all around us the impossible wealth
and glory of this earth, feeling with an intolerable
certitude that the whole structure of the enchanted life
—the most fortunate, wealthy, good, and happy life that
any man has ever known—is ours—is ours at once, imme-

diately and forever, the moment that we choose to take a step, or stretch a hand, or say a word—we yet know that we can really keep, hold, take, and possess forever —nothing. All passes; nothing lasts: the moment that we put our hand upon it it melts away like smoke, is gone forever, and the snake is eating at our heart again; we see then what we are and what our lives must come to.

A young man is so strong, so mad, so certain, and so lost. He has everything and he is able to use nothing. He hurls the great shoulder of his strength forever against phantasmal barriers, he is a wave whose power explodes in lost mid-oceans under timeless skies, he reaches out to grip a fume of painted smoke; he wants all, feels the thirst and power for everything, and finally gets nothing. In the end, he is destroyed by his own strength, devoured by his own hunger, impoverished by his own wealth. Thoughtless of money or the accumulation of material possessions, he is none the less defeated in the end by his own greed—a greed that makes the avarice of King Midas seem paltry by comparison.

And that is the reason why, when youth is gone, every man will look back upon that period of his life with infinite sorrow and regret. It is the bitter sorrow and regret of a man who knows that once he had a great talent and wasted it, of a man who knows that once he had a great treasure and got nothing from it, of a man who knows that he had strength enough for everything and never used it.

The Earth Flows By

ON EVERYTHING—trees, houses, foliage, yards, and street there was a curious loneliness of departure and October, an attentive almost mournful waiting. And yet this dark and dusty street of the tall trees left a haunting, curiously pleasant feeling of strangeness and familiarity. One viewed it with a queer sudden ache in the heart, a feeling of friendship and farewell, and this feeling was probably intensified by the swift and powerful movement of the train which seemed to slide past the town almost noiselessly, its wheels turning without friction, sound, or vibrance on the pressed steel ribbons of the rails, giving to a traveller, and particularly to a youth who was going into the secret North for the first time, a feeling of illimitable and exultant power, evoking for him the huge mystery of the night and darkness, and the image of ten thousand lonely little towns like this across the continent.

Then the train slides by the darkened vacant-looking little station and for a moment one has a glimpse of the town's chief square and business centre. And as he sees it he is filled again with the same feeling of loneliness, instant familiarity, and departure. The square is one of those anomalous, shabby-ornate, inept, and pitifully pretentious places that one finds in little towns like these. But once seen, if only for this fraction of a moment, from the windows of a train, the memory of it will haunt one forever after.

And this haunting and lonely memory is due probably to the combination of two things: the ghastly imitation of swarming life and metropolitan gaiety in the scene, and the almost total absence of life itself. The impression one gets, in fact, from that brief vision is one of frozen cataleptic silence in a world from which all life has recently been extinguished by some appalling catastrophe. The lights burn, the electric signs wink and flash, the place is still horribly intact in all its bleak prognathous newness, but all the people are dead, gone, vanished. The place is a tomb of frozen silence, as terrifying in its empty bleakness as those advertising backdrops one saw formerly in theatres, where the splendid buildings, stores, and shops of a great street are painted in the richest and most flattering colors, and where there is no sign of life whatever.

So was it here, save that here the illusion of the dead world gained a hideous physical reality by its stark, staring, nakedly concrete dimensions.

All this the boy had seen, or rather sensed, in the wink of an eye, a moment's vision of a dusty little street, a fleeting glimpse of a silent little square, a few hard lights, and then the darkness of the earth again—these half-splintered glimpses were all the boy could really see in the eye-wink that it took the train to pass the town. And yet, all these fragmentary things belonged so completely to all the life of little towns which he had known, that it was not as if he had seen only a few splintered images, but rather as if the whole nocturnal picture of the town was instantly whole and living in his mind.

Beyond the station, parked in a line against the curb is a row of empty motor cars, and he knows instantly that they have been left there by the patrons of the little moving-picture theatre which explodes out of the cataleptic silence of the left-hand side of the square into a blaze of hard white and flaming posters which seem to cover the entire façade. Even here, no movement of life is visible, but one who has lived and known towns like these feels for the first time an emotion of warmth and life as he looks at the gaudy, blazing bill-beplastered silence of that front.

For suddenly he seems to see the bluish blaze of carbon light that comes from the small slit-like vent-hole cut into the wall and can hear again—one of the loneliest and most haunting of all sounds—the rapid shuttering sound of the projection camera late at night, a sound lonely, hurried, unforgettable, coming out into those cataleptic squares of silence in the little towns— as if the operator is fairly racing through the last performance of the night like a weary and exhausted creature whose stale, over-driven life can find no joy in what is giving so much joy to others, and who is pressing desperately ahead toward the merciful rewards of food, sleep, and oblivion which are already almost in his grasp.

And as he remembers this, he also suddenly sees and knows the people in the theatre, and in that instant greets them, feels his lonely kinship with them, with the whole family of the earth, and says farewell. Small, dark, lonely, silent, thirsty, and insatiate, the people of the little town are gathered there in that one small cell of radiance, warmth, and joy. There for a little space they are united by the magic spell the theatre casts upon them. They are all dark and silent, leaning forward like a single mind and congeries of life, and yet they are all separate too.

Yes, lonely, silent, for a moment beautiful, he knows the people of the town are there, lifting the small white petals of their faces, thirsty and insatiate, to that magic screen: now they laugh exultantly as their hero triumphs, weep quietly as the mother dies, the little boys cheer wildly as the rascal gets his due—they are all there in darkness under immense immortal skies of time, small

nameless creatures in a lost town on the mighty continent, and for an instant we have seen them, known
them, said farewell.

Around the four sides of the square at even intervals,
the new standards of the five-bulbed lamps cast down
implacably upon those cataleptic pavements the cataleptic silence of their hard white light. And this, he
knows, is called "the Great White Way," of which the
town is proud. Somehow the ghastly, lifeless silence of
that little square is imaged nowhere else so cruelly as
in the harsh, white silence of these lights. For they evoke
terribly, as nothing else can do, the ghastly vacancy
of light without life. And poignantly, pitifully, and unutterably their harsh, white silence evokes the moth-
like hunger of the American for hard, brilliant, blazing incandescence.

It is as if there may be in his soul the horror of the
ancient darkness, the terror of the old immortal silences,
which will not down and must be heard. It is as if he
feels again the ancient fear of—what? Of the wilderness,
the wet and lidless eye of shame and desolation feeding
always on unhoused and naked sides. It is as if he fears
the brutal revelation of his loss and loneliness, the
furious, irremediable confusion of his huge unrest, his
desperate and unceasing flight from the immense and
timeless skies that bend above him, the huge, doorless
and unmeasured vacancies of distance, on which he
lives, on which, as helpless as a leaf upon a hurricane,
he is driven on forever, and on which he cannot pause,
which he cannot fence, wall, conquer, make his own.

Then the train, running always with its smooth, powerful, almost noiseless movement, has left the station and the square behind it. The last outposts of the town appear and vanish in patterns of small, lonely light, and there is nothing but huge and secret night before us, the lonely, everlasting earth, and presently Virginia.

And surely, now, there is little more to be seen. Surely, now, there is almost nothing that by day would be worthy of more than a glance from those great travellers who have ranged the earth, and known all its wild and stormy seas, and seen its rarest glories. And by night, now, there is nothing, nothing by night but darkness and a space we call Virginia, through which the huge projectile of the train is hurtling onward in the dark.

The Lost Land

STRANGE aerial music came fluting out of darkness, or over his slow-wakening senses swept the great waves of symphonic orchestration. Fiendvoices, beautiful and sleep-loud, called down through darkness and light, developing the thread of ancient memory.

Staggering blindly in the whitewashed glare, his eyes, sleep-corded, opened slowly as he was born anew, umbilically cut, from darkness.

Waken, ghost-eared boy, but into darkness. Waken, phantom, O into us. Try, try, O try the way. Open the wall of light. Ghost, ghost, who is the ghost? O lost. Ghost, ghost, who is the ghost? O whisper-tongued laughter. Eugene! Eugene! Here, O here, Eugene. Here, Eugene. The way is here, Eugene. Have you forgotten? The leaf, the rock, the wall of light. Lift up the rock, Eugene, the leaf, the stone, the unfound door. Return, return.

A voice, sleep-strange and loud, forever far-near, spoke.

Eugene!

Spoke, ceased, continued without speaking, to speak.

In him spoke. Where darkness, son, is light. Try, boy, the word you know remember. In the beginning was the logos. Over the border the borderless green-forested land. Yesterday, remember?

Far-forested, a horn-note wound. Sea-forested, water-far, the grottoed coral sea-far horn-note. The pillioned ladies witch-faced in bottle-green robes saddle-swinging. Merwomen unscaled and lovely in sea-floor colonnades. The hidden land below the rock. The flitting wood-girls growing into bark. Far-faint, as he wakened, they besought him with lessening whir. Then deeper song, fiend-throated, wind-shod. Brother, O brother! They shot down the brink of darkness, gone on the wind like bullets. O lost, and by the wind grieved, ghost, come back again.

Lost Country of Youth

IN MORNING sunlight on a hospital porch, five flights
above the ground, an old dying spectre of a man
was sitting, looking mournfully out across the sun-
hazed sweep of the city he had known in his youth.
He sat there, a rusty, creaking hinge, an almost severed

thread of life, a shockingly wasted integument of skin and bone, of which every fibre and sinew was almost utterly rotted out, consumed and honey-combed by the great plant of the cancer which flowered from his entrails and had now spread its fibrous roots to every tissue of his life. Everything was gone: everything was wasted from him: the face was drawn tight and bony as a beak, the skin was clean, tinged with a fatal cancerous yellow, and almost delicately transparent. The great thin blade of nose cut down across the face with knifelike sharpness and in the bony, slanting, almost reptilian cage-formation of the skull, the smallish cold-gray-green eyes were set wearily, with a wretched and enfeebled dullness, out across the great space of the city which swept away and melted at length into the sun-hazed vistas of October.

Nothing was left but his hands. The rest of the man was dead. But the great hands of the stonecutter, on whose sinewy and bony substance there was so little that disease or death could waste, looked as powerful and living as ever. Although one of his hands—the right one—had been stiffened years before by an attack of rheumatism, they had lost none of their character of power and massive shapeliness.

In the huge shapely knuckles, in the length and sinewy thickness of the great fingers—which were twice the size of an ordinary man's—and in the whole length and sinewy contour of the hand, there was a quality of sculptural design which was as solid and proportionate as any of the marble hands of love and grace which the stonecutter had so often carved upon the surface of a grave-yard monument.

Thus, as he sat there now, staring dully out across the city, an emaciated and phantasmal shadow of a man, there was, in the appearance of these great living hands of power (one of which lay with an enormous passive grace and dignity across the arm of his chair and the other extended and clasped down upon the handle of a walking stick), something weirdly incongruous, as if the great strong hands had been unnaturally attached to the puny lifeless figure of a scarecrow.

Now, wearily, desperately, the old enfeebled mind was trying to grope with the strange and bitter miracle of life, to get some meaning out of that black, senseless fusion of pain and joy and agony, that web that had known all the hope and joy and wonder of a boy, the fury, passion, drunkenness, and wild desire of youth, the rich adventure and fulfilment of a man, and that had led him to this fatal and abominable end.

But that fading, pain-sick mind, that darkened memory could draw no meaning and no comfort from its tragic meditation.

The old man's land of youth was far away in time, yet now only the magic lonely hills of his life's journey, his wife's people, seemed sorrowful, lonely, lost, and strange to him. Now he remembered all places, things, and people in his land of youth as if he had known them instantly and forever!

Oh, what a land, a life, a time was that—that world of youth and no return. What colors of green-gold, magic, rich plantations, and shining cities were in it! For now, when this dying man thought about this vanished life, that tragic quality of sorrow and loneliness had vanished instantly. All that he had read in books about old wars seemed far and lost and in another time, but when he thought about these things that he had known as a boy, he saw them instantly, knew them, breathed them, heard them, felt them, was there beside them, living them with his own life. He remembered now his wife's people!—tramping in along the Carlisle Pike on that hot first morning in July, as they marched in towards Gettysburg. He had been standing there with his next older brother Gil, beside the dusty road, as they came by.

And he could see them now, not as shadowy, lost, phantasmal figures of dark time, the way they were in books; he saw them, heard them, knew them again as they had been in their shapeless rags of uniforms, their bare feet wound in rags, their lank disordered hair, sometimes topped by stove-pipe hats which they had looted out of stores.

"God!" the old man thought, wetting his great thumb briefly, grinning thinly, as he shook his head, "What a scarecrow crew that was! In all my days I never saw the like of it! A bum-looking lot, if ever there was one! —And the bravest of the brave, the finest troops that ever lived!"—his mind swung upward to its tide of rhetoric—"Veterans all of them, who had been through the bloodiest battles of the war, they did not know the meaning of the word 'fear,' and they would have gone into the valley of death, the jaws of hell, at a word from their Commander!" His mind was alive again, in full swing now, the old voice rose and muttered on the tides of rhetoric, the great hand gestured, the cold-gray, restless eyes glared feverishly about—and all of it began to live for him again.

He remembered how he and Gil had been standing there beside the road, two barefoot farmer boys, aged thirteen and fifteen, and he remembered how the Rebels would halt upon their march, and shout jesting remarks at the two boys standing at the road. One shouted out to Gil:

"Hi, there, Yank! You'd better hide! Jeb Stuart's on the way an' he's been lookin' fer you!"

And Gil, older, bolder, more assured than he, quick-tempered, stubborn, fiercely partisan, had come back like a flash:

"He'll be lookin' fer *you* when we get through with you!" said Gil and the Rebels had slapped their ragged thighs and howled with laughter, shouting at their crest-fallen, grinning comrade:

" 'Y, God! I reckon you'll be quiet now! He shore God put it on ye that time!"

And he was there beside his brother, seeing, hearing, living it again, as he remembered his strange first meeting with the Pentland tribe, the haunting miracle of that chance meeting. For among that ragged crew he had first seen his wife's uncle, the prophet, Bacchus Pentland, and he had seen him, heard him that hot morning, and had never been able to forget him, although it would be twenty years, after many strange turnings of the roads of destiny and wandering, before he was to see the man again, and know his name, and join together the two halves of fated meeting.

Yes, there had been one among the drawling and terrible mountaineers that day who passed there on that dusty road, and paused, and talked, and waited in the heat, one whose face he had never been able to forget—one whose full, ruddy face and tranquil eyes were lighted always by a smile of idiot and beatific saint-liness, whose powerful fleshy body gave off a stench that would have put a goat to shame, and who on this account was called by his jesting comrades, "Stinking Jesus." Yes, he had been there that morning, Bacchus Pentland, the fated and chosen of God, the supernatural appearer on roads at nightfall, the harbinger of death, the prophet, chanting even then his promises of Ar-mageddon and the Coming of the Lord, speaking for the first time to the fascinated ears of those two boys, the full, drawling, unctuous accents of the fated, time-triumphant Pentlands.

They came, they halted in the dust before the two young brothers, the lewd tongues mocked and jested, but that man of God, the prophet Bacchus Pentland, was beautifully unmoved by their unfaith, and chanted, with a smile of idiot beatitude, his glorious assurances of an end of death and battle, everlasting peace:

"Hit's a comin'!" cried the prophet with the sweet purity of his saintly smile. "Hit's a comin'! Accordin' to my figgers the Great Day is almost here! Oh, hit's a comin', boys!" he sweetly, cheerfully intoned, "Christ's kingdom on this airth's at hand! We're marchin' in to Armageddon now!"

"Hell, Back!" drawled one, with a slow grin of disbelief. "You said the same thing afore Chancellorsville, an' all I got from it was a slug of canister in my tail!" —and the others slapped their ragged thighs and shouted.

"Hit's a comin'!" Bacchus cried, with a brisk wink, and his seraphic smile, unmoved, untouched, by their derision. "He'll be here a-judgin' an' decreein' afore the week is over, settin' up His Kingdom, an' sortin' us all out the way it was foretold—the sheep upon His right hand an' the goats upon His left."

"An' which side are you goin' to be on, Back, when all this sortin' starts?" one drawled with evil innocence. "Are you goin' to be upon the sheep-side or the goat-side?" he demanded.

"Oh," cried Bacchus cheerfully, with his seraphic smile, "I'll be upon the sheep-side, brother, with the Chosen of the Lord."

"Then, Back," the other slowly answered, "you'd shore God better begin to smell a whole lot better than you do right now, for if the Lord starts sortin' in the dark, Back, He's goin' to put you where you don't belong—He'll have you over thar among the goats!"— and the hot brooding air had rung then with their roars of laughter. Then a word was spoken, an order given, the ragged files trudged on again, and they were gone.

Now this was lost, a fume of smoke, the moment's image of a fading memory, and he could not say it, speak it, find a word for it—but he could see that boy of his lost youth as he sat round the kitchen table with the rest of them. He could see his cold-gray, restless, unhappy eyes, the strange, gaunt, almost reptilian conformation of his staring face, his incredibly thin, blade-like nose, as he waited there in silence, looking uneasily at the others with his cold-gray, shallow, most unhappy eyes. And the old man seemed to be the spy of destiny, to look at once below the roofs of a million little houses everywhere and on the star-shone, death-flung mystery of the silent battlefield.

He seemed to be a witness of the secret weavings of dark chance that threads our million lives into strange purposes that we do not know. He thought of those dead and wounded men upon the battlefield whose lives would touch his own so nearly, the wounded brother that he knew, the wounded stranger he had seen that day by magic chance, whom he could not forget, and whose life, whose tribe, in the huge abyss and secret purpose of dark time, would one day interweave into his own.

Oh, he could not find a word, a phrase to utter it, but he seemed to have the lives not only of those people in him, but the lives of millions of others whose dark fate is thus determined, interwove, and beyond their vision or their knowledge, foredone and made inevitable in the dark destiny of unfathomed time. And suddenly it seemed to him that all of it was his, even as his father's blood and earth was his, the lives and deaths and destinies of all his people. He had been a nameless atom in the great family of earth, a single, unknown thread in the huge warp of fate and chance that weaves our lives together, and because of this he had been the richest man that ever lived; the power, grandeur, glory of this earth and all its lives of men were his.

And for a moment he forgot that he was old and dying, and pride, joy, pain, triumphant ecstasy that had no tongue to utter it rose like a wordless swelling pæan in his throat, because it seemed to him that this great familiar earth on which his people lived and wrought was his, that all the mystery, grandeur and beauty in the lives of men were his, and that he must find a word, a tongue, a door to utter what was his, or die!

How could he say it! How could he ever find a word to speak the joy, the pain, the grandeur bursting in the great vine of his heart, swelling like a huge grape in his throat—mad, sweet, wild, intolerable with all the mystery, loneliness, wild secret joy, and death, the ever-returning and renewing fruitfulness of the earth!

A cloud-shadow passed and left no light but loneliness on the massed green of the wilderness! A bird was calling in a secret wood! And there was something going, coming, fading there across the sun—oh, there was something lonely and most sorrowful, his mother's voice, the voices of lost men long, long ago, the flowing of a little river in the month of April—and all, all of it was his!

[94]

He had stood beside a dusty road, feet bare, his gaunt boy's face cold-eyed, staring, restless, and afraid. The ragged jesting Rebels passed before him in the dusty heat, the huge drowse and cricketing stitch of noon was rising from the sweet woods and nobly swelling, fertile fields of Pennsylvania and all, all, all of it was his!

A prophet passed before him in the road that day with the familiar haunting unction of an unmet, unheard tribe; a wounded prophet lay that night below the stars and chanted glory, peace, and Armageddon; the boy's brother lay beside the prophet bleeding from the lungs; the boy's people grimly waited all night long in a little house not fourteen miles away; and all, all, all of it was his!

Over the wild and secret earth, the lonely, everlasting, and unchanging earth, under the huge tent of the all-engulfing night, amid the fury, chaos, blind confusions of a hundred million lives, something wild and secret had been weaving through the generations, a dark terrific weaving of the threads of time and destiny.

But it had come to this: an old man dying on a porch, staring through the sun-hazed vistas of October towards the lost country of his youth.

This was the end of man, then, end of life, of fury, hope, and passion, glory, all the strange and bitter miracle of chance, of history, fate, and destiny which even a stonecutter's life could include. This was the end, then:—an old man, feeble, foul, complaining and disease-consumed, who sat looking from the high porch of a hospital at the city of his youth. This was the sicken-

Destiny

EACH of us is all the sums he has not counted: subtract us into nakedness and night again, and you shall see begin in Crete four thousand years ago the love that ended yesterday in Texas.

The seed of our destruction will blossom in the desert, the alexin of our cure grows by a mountain rock, and our lives are haunted by a Georgia slattern, because a London cutpurse went unhung. Each moment is the fruit of forty thousand years. The minute-winning days, like flies, buzz home to death, and every moment is a window on all time.

Portrait

AS HIS mind groped out of the pain of impression he heard her voice and, still feeling within him the strange convulsive shame, he lifted his eyes to her face. It was the most tranquil and the most passionate face he had ever seen. The skin was sallow with a dead ashen tinge; beneath, the delicate bone-carving of face and skull traced itself clearly: the cadaverous tightness of those who are about to die had been checked. She had won her way back just far enough to balance carefully in the scales of disease and recovery. It was necessary for her to measure everything she did.

Her thin face was given a touch of shrewdness and decision by the straight line of her nose, the fine long carving of her chin. Beneath the sallow minutely pitted skin in her cheeks, and about her mouth, several frayed nerve-centres twitched from moment to moment, jarring the skin slightly without contorting or destroying the passionate calm beauty that fed her inexhaustibly from within. This face was the constant field of conflict, nearly always calm, but always reflecting the incessant struggle and victory of the enormous energy that inhabited her, over the thousand jangling devils of depletion and weariness that tried to pull her apart. There was always written upon her the epic poetry of beauty and repose out of struggle—he never ceased to feel that she had her hand around the reins of her heart, that gathered into her grasp were all the straining wires and sinews of disunion which would scatter and unjoint her members, once she let go. Literally, physically, he felt that, the great tide of valiance once flowed out of her, she would immediately go to pieces.

She was like some great general, famous, tranquil, wounded unto death, who, with his fingers clamped across a severed artery, stops for an hour the ebbing of his life—sends on the battle.

Her hair was coarse and dull-brown, fairly abundant, tinged lightly with gray: it was combed evenly in the middle and bound tightly in a knot behind. Everything about her was very clean, like a scrubbed kitchen board: she took his hand, he felt the firm nervous vitality of her fingers, and he noticed how clean and scrubbed her thin somewhat labor-worn hands were. If he noticed her emaciation at all now, it was only with a sense of her purification: he felt himself in union not with disease, but with the greatest health he had ever known. She made a high music in him. His heart lifted.

Her face darkened with the strange passionate vitality that left no print, that lived there bodiless like life; her brown eyes darkened into black as if a bird had flown through them and left the shadow of its wings. She saw his small remote face burning strangely at the end of his long unfleshed body, she saw the straight thin shanks, the big feet turned awkwardly inward, the dusty patches on his stockings at the knees, and his thin wristy arms that stuck out painfully below his cheap ill-fitting jacket; she saw the thin hunched line of his shoulders, the tangled mass of hair—and she did not laugh.

He turned his face up to her as a prisoner who recovers light, as a man long pent in darkness who bathes himself in the great pool of dawn, as a blind man who feels upon his eyes the white core and essence of immutable brightness. His body drank in her great light as a famished castaway the rain: he closed his eyes and let the great light bathe him, and when he opened them again, he saw that her own were luminous and wet.

Lonely Joy

B UT they danced there slowly in a gray light of
dusk that was like pain and beauty; like the lost
light undersea, in which his life, a lost merman,
swam, remembering exile. And as they danced
she, whom he dared not touch, yielded her body unto
him, whispering softly to his ear, pressing with slender
fingers his hot hand. And she, whom he would not touch,
lay there, like a sheaf of grain, in the crook of his arm,
token of the world's remedy—the refuge from the one
lost face out of all the faces, the anodyne against the
wound named Laura—a thousand flitting shapes of
beauty to bring him comfort and delight. The great
pageantry of pain and pride and death hung through
the dusk its awful vision, touching his sorrow with a
lonely joy. He had lost; but all pilgrimage across the
world was loss: a moment of cleaving, a moment of taking away, the thousand phantom shapes that beaconed,
and the high impassionate grief of stars.

The Dream of Time

O KEEP time with!"
What is this dream of time, this strange and
bitter miracle of living? Is it the wind that
drives the leaves down bare paths fleeing? Is it
the storm-wild flight of furious days, the storm-swift
passing of the million faces, all lost, forgotten, vanished
as a dream? Is it the wind that howls above the earth,
is it the wind that drives all things before its lash, is it
the wind that drives all men like dead ghosts fleeing?
Is it that one red leaf that strains there on the bough and
that forever will be fleeing? All things are lost and
broken in the wind: the dry leaves scamper down the
path before us, in their swift-winged dance of death the

dead souls flee along before us driven with rusty scuffle before the fury of the demented wind. And October has come again, has come again.

What is this strange and bitter miracle of life? Is it to feel, when furious day is done, the evening hush, the sorrow of lost, fading light, far sounds and broken cries, and footsteps, voices, music, and all lost—and something murmurous, immense and mighty in the air?

And we have walked the pavements of a little town and known the passages of barren night, and heard the wheel, the whistle and the tolling bell, and lain in the darkness waiting, giving to silence the huge prayer of our intolerable desire. And we have heard the sorrowful silence of the river in October—and what is there to say? October has come again, has come again, and this world, this life, this time are stranger than a dream.

May it not be that some day from this dream of time, this chronicle of smoke, this strange and bitter miracle of life in which we are the moving and phantasmal figures, we shall wake? Knowing our father's voice upon the porch again, the flowers, the grapevines, the low rich moons of waning August, and the tolling bell—and instantly to know we live, that we have dreamed and have awakened, and find then in our hands some object, like this real and palpable, some gift out of the lost land and the unknown world as token that it was no dream—that we have really been there? And there is no more to say.

For now October has come back again, the strange

[103]

and lonely month comes back again, and you will not return.

Up on the mountain, down in the valley, deep, deep, in the hill, Ben—cold, cold, cold.

"To keep time with!"

And suddenly the scene, the shapes, the voices of the men about him swam back into their focus, and he could hear the rhythmed pounding of the wheels below him, and in his palm the frail-numbered visage of the watch stared blank and plain at him its legend. It was one minute after twelve o'clock, Sunday morning, October the third, 1920, and he was hurtling across Virginia, and this world, this life, this time were stranger than a dream.

The Heart of the Dark

THE face of the night, the heart of the dark, the tongue of the flame—I had known all things that lived or stirred or worked below her destiny. I was the child of night, a son among her mighty family, and I knew all that moved within the hearts of men who loved the night. I had seen them in a thousand places and nothing that they ever did or said was strange to me. As a child, when I had been a route boy on a morning paper, I had seen them on the streets of a little town—that strange and lonely company of men who prowl the night. Sometimes they were alone, and sometimes they went together in a group of two or three, forever in midwatches of the night in little towns prowling up and down the empty pavements of bleak streets, passing before the ghastly waxen models in the windows of the clothing stores, passing below hard bulbous clusters of white light, prowling before the façades of a hundred darkened stores, pausing at length in some little lunch-room to drawl and gossip quietly, to thrust snout, lip, and sallow jowl into the stained depths of a coffee mug, or dully to wear the slow gray ash of time away without a word.

The memory of their faces, and their restless prowling of the night, familiar and unquestioned at the time, returned now with the strangeness of a dream. What did they want? What had they hoped to find as they prowled past a thousand doors in those little, bleak, and wintry towns?

Their hope, their wild belief, the dark song that the night awoke in them, this thing that lived in darkness while men slept and knew a secret and exultant triumph, and that was everywhere across the land, were written in my heart. Not in the purity and sweetness of dawn with all the brave and poignant glory of its revelation, nor in the practical and homely lights of morning, nor in the silent stature of the corn at noon, the drowsy hum and stitch of three o'clock across the fields, nor in the strange magic gold and green of its wild lyric wooded earth, nor even in the land that breathed quietly the last heat and violence of day away into the fathomless depth and brooding stillness of the dusk—as brave and glorious as these times and lights had been—had I felt and found the mystery, the grandeur, and the immortal beauty of America.

I had found the dark land at the heart of night, of dark, proud, secret night: the immense and lonely land lived for me in the brain of night. I saw its plains, its rivers, and its mountains spread out before me in all their dark immortal beauty, in all the space and joy of their huge sweep, in all their loneliness, savagery, and terror, and in all their immense and delicate fecundity. And my heart was one with the hearts of all men who had heard the strange wild music that they made, filled with unknown harmonies and a thousand wild and secret tongues crying to men the exultant and terrible music of wild earth, triumph and discovery, singing a strange and bitter prophecy of love and death.

For there was something living on the land at night. There was a dark tide moving in the hearts of men. Wild, strange and jubilant, sweeping on across the immense and sleeping earth, it had spoken to me in a thousand watches of the night, and the language of all its dark and secret tongues was written in my heart. It had passed above me with the rhythmical sustentions of its mighty wing, it had shot away with bullet cries of a demonic ecstasy on the swift howlings of the winter wind, it had come softly, numbly, with a dark impending prescience of wild joy in the dull soft skies of coming snow, and it had brooded, dark and wild and secret, in the night, across the land, and over the tremendous and dynamic silence of the city, stilled in its million cells of sleep, trembling forever in the night with the murmurous, remote and mighty sound of time.

And I was joined in knowledge and in life with an

indubitable certitude to the great company of men who lived by night and had known and loved its mystery. I had known all joys and labors and designs that such men know. I had known all things living on the earth by night, and finally, I had known by night the immortal fellowship of those three with whom the best part of my life was passed—proud Death, and his stern brother, Loneliness, and their great sister, Sleep. I had lived and worked and wrought alone with Loneliness, my friend, and in the darkness, in the night, in all the sleeping silence of the earth, I had looked a thousand times into the visages of Sleep, and had heard the sound of her dark horses when they came. And I had watched my brother and my father die in the dark midwatches of the night, and I had known and loved the figure of proud Death when he had come.

Hunger to Devour the Earth

T HE train rushed on across the brown autumnal
land, by wink of water and the rocky coasts,
the small white towns and flaming colors and
the lonely, tragic and eternal beauty of New
England. It was the country of his heart's desire, the

[109]

dark Helen in his blood forever burning—and now the fast approach across October land, the engine smoke that streaked back on the sharp gray air that day!

The coming on of the great earth, the new lands, the enchanted city, the approach, so smoky, blind and stifled, to the ancient web, the old grimed thrilling barricades of Boston. The streets and buildings that slid past that day with such a haunting strange familiarity, the mighty engine steaming to its halt, and the great train-shed dense with smoke and acrid with its smell and full of the slow pantings of a dozen engines, now passive as great cats, the mighty station with the ceaseless throngings of its illimitable life, and all of the murmurous, remote and mighty sounds of time forever held there in the station, together with a tart and nasal voice, a hand'sbreadth off that said: "There's hahdly time, but try it if you want."

He saw the narrow, twisted, age-browned streets of Boston, then, with their sultry fragrance of fresh-roasted coffee, the sight of the man-swarm passing in its million-footed weft, the distant drone and murmur of the great mysterious city all about him, the shining water of the Basin, and the murmur of the harbor and its ships, the promise of glory and of a thousand secret, lovely and mysterious women that were waiting somewhere in the city's web.

He saw the furious streets of life with their unending flood-tide of a million faces, the enormous library with its million books; or was it just one moment in the flood-tide of the city, at five o'clock, a voice, a face, a brawny lusty girl with smiling mouth who passed him in an instant at the Park Street station, stood printed in the strong October wind a moment—breast, belly, arm, and thigh, and all her brawny lustihood—and then had gone into the man-swarm, lost forever, never found?

Was it at such a moment—engine-smoke, a station, a street, the sound of time, a face that came and passed and vanished, could not be forgot—*here* or *here* or *here,* at such a moment of man's unrecorded memory, that he breathed fury from the air, that fury came?

He never knew; but now mad fury gripped his life, and he was haunted by the dream of time. Ten years must come and go without a moment's rest from fury, ten years of fury, hunger, all of the wandering in a young man's life. And for what? For what?

What is the fury which this youth will feel, which will lash him on against the great earth forever? It is the brain that maddens with its own excess, the heart that breaks from the anguish of its own frustration. It is the hunger that grows from everything it feeds upon, the thirst that gulps down rivers and remains insatiate. It is to see a million men, a million faces and to be a stranger and an alien to them always. It is to prowl the stacks of an enormous library at night, to tear the books out of a thousand shelves, to read in them with the mad hunger of the youth of man.

It is to have the old unquiet mind, the famished heart, the restless soul; it is to lose hope, heart, and all joy utterly, and then to have them wake again, to have the old feeling return with overwhelming force that he

is about to find the thing for which his life obscurely
and desperately is groping—for which all men on this
earth have sought—one face out of the million faces,
a wall, a door, a place of certitude and peace and wandering no more. For what is it that we Americans are
seeking always on this earth? Why is it we have crossed
the stormy seas so many times alone, lain in a thousand
alien rooms at night hearing the sounds of time, dark
time, and thought until heart, brain, flesh and spirit
were sick and weary with the thought of it; "Where
shall I go now? What shall I do?"

He did not know the moment that it came, but it
came instantly, at once. And from that moment on mad
fury seized him, from that moment on, his life, more
than the life of any one that he would ever know, was
to be spent in solitude and wandering. Why this was
true, or how it happened, he would never know; yet it
was so. From this time on—save for two intervals in his
life—he was to live about as solitary a life as a modern
man can have. And it is meant by this that the number
of hours, days, months, and years—the actual time he
spent alone—would be immense and extraordinary.

And this fact was all the more astonishing because he
never seemed to seek out solitude, nor did he shrink from
life, or seek to build himself into a wall away from all
the fury and the turmoil of the earth. Rather, he loved
life so dearly that he was driven mad by the thirst and
hunger which he felt for it. Of this fury, which was to
lash and drive him on for fifteen years, the thousandth

the ten thousands, yet he had no desire to be bookish; no one could describe this mad assault upon print as scholarly: a ravening appetite in him demanded that he read everything that had ever been written about human experience. He read no more from pleasure— the thought that other books were waiting for him tore at his heart forever. He pictured himself as tearing the entrails from a book as from a fowl. At first, hovering over book stalls, or walking at night among the vast piled shelves of the library, he would read, watch in hand, muttering to himself in triumph or anger at the timing of each page: "Fifty seconds to do that one. Damn you, we'll see! You will, will you?"—and he would tear through the next page in twenty seconds.

This fury which drove him on to read so many books had nothing to do with scholarship, nothing to do with academic honors, nothing to do with formal learning. He was not in any way a scholar and did not want to be one. He simply wanted to know about everything on earth; he wanted to devour the earth, and it drove him mad when he saw he could not do this. And it was the same with everything he did. In the midst of a furious burst of reading in the enormous library, the thought of the streets outside and the great city all around him would drive through his body like a sword. It would now seem to him that every second that he passed among the books was being wasted—that at this moment something priceless, irrecoverable was happening in the streets, and that if only he could get to it in time and see it, he would somehow get the knowledge of the whole thing in him—the source, the well, the spring from which all men and words and actions, and every design upon this earth proceeds.

And he would rush out in the streets to find it, be hurled through the tunnel into Boston and then spend hours in driving himself savagely through a hundred streets, looking into the faces of a million people, trying to get an instant and conclusive picture of all they did and said and were, of all their million destinies, and of the great city and the everlasting earth, and the immense and lonely skies that bent above them. And he would search the furious streets until bone and brain and blood could stand no more—until every sinew of his life and spirit was wrung, trembling and exhausted, and his heart sank down beneath its weight of desolation and despair.

Yet a furious hope, a wild extravagant belief, was burning in him all the time. He would write down enormous charts and plans and projects of all that he proposed to do in life—a program of work and living which would have exhausted the energies of 10,000 men. He would get up in the middle of the night to scrawl down insane catalogs of all that he had seen and done:—the number of books he had read, the number of miles he had travelled, the number of people he had known, the number of women he had slept with, the number of meals he had eaten, the number of towns he had visited, the number of states he had been in.

And at one moment he would gloat and chuckle over these stupendous lists like a miser gloating over his hoard, only to groan bitterly with despair the next moment, and to beat his head against the wall, as he remembered the overwhelming amount of all he had not seen or done, or known. Then he would begin another list filled with enormous catalogs of all the books he had not read, all the food he had not eaten, all the women that he had not slept with, all the states he had not been in, all the towns he had not visited. Then he would write down plans and programs whereby all these things must be accomplished, how many years it would take to do it all, and how old he would be when he had finished. An enormous wave of hope and joy would surge up in him, because it now looked easy, and he had no doubt at all that he could do it.

He never asked himself in any practical way how he was going to live while this was going on, where he was going to get the money for this gigantic adventure, and what he was going to do to make it possible. If he thought about it, it seemed to have no importance or reality whatever—he just dismissed it impatiently, or with a conviction that some old man would die and leave him a fortune, that he was going to pick up a purse containing hundreds of thousands of dollars while walking in the Fenway, and that the reward would be enough to keep him going, or that a beautiful and rich young widow, true-hearted, tender, loving, and voluptuous, who had carrot-colored hair, little freckles on her face, a snub nose and luminous gray-green eyes with something wicked yet loving and faithful in them, and one gold filling in her solid little teeth, was going

to fall in love with him, marry him, and be forever true
and faithful to him while he went reading, eating,
drinking, whoring, and devouring his way around the
world; or finally that he would write a book or play
every year or so, which would be a great success, and
yield him fifteen or twenty thousand dollars at a crack.
Thus, he went storming away at the whole earth about
him, sometimes mad with despair, weariness, and be-
wilderment; and sometimes wild with a jubilant and
exultant joy and certitude as the conviction came to
him that everything would happen as he wished. Then
at night he would hear the vast sounds and silence of
the earth and of the city, he would begin to think of
the dark sleeping earth and of the continent of night,
until it seemed to him it all was spread before him like a
map—rivers, plains, and mountains and 10,000 sleeping
towns; it seemed to him that he saw everything at once.

Coming of Spring

Yes, and in that month when Proserpine comes back, and Ceres' dead heart rekindles, when all the woods are a tender smoky blur, and birds no bigger than a budding leaf dart through the singing trees, and when odorous tar comes spongy in the streets, and boys roll balls of it upon their tongues, and they are lumpy with tops and agated marbles; and there is blasting thunder in the night, and the soaking million-footed rain, and one looks out at morning on a stormy sky, a broken wrack of cloud; and when the mountain boy brings water to his kinsmen laying fence, and as the wind snakes through the grasses hears far in the valley below the long wail of the whistle, and the faint clangor of a bell; and the blue great cup of the hills seems closer, nearer, for he has heard an inarticulate promise: he has been pierced by Spring, that sharp knife.

And life unscales its rusty weathered pelt and earth wells out in tender exhaustless strength, and the cup of a man's heart runs over with dateless expectancy, tongueless promise, indefinable desire. Something gathers in the throat, something blinds him in the eyes, and faint and valorous horns sound through the earth.

The little girls trot pigtailed primly on their dutiful way to school; but the young gods loiter: they hear the reed, the oaten-stop, the running goathoofs in the spongy wood, here, there, everywhere: they dawdle, listen, fleetest when they wait, go vaguely on to their one fixed home, because the earth is full of ancient rumor and they cannot find the way. All of the gods have lost the way.

Proud, Cruel City

P ROUD, cruel, everchanging and ephemeral city, to whom we came once when our hearts were high, our blood passionate and hot, our brain a particle of fire: infinite and mutable city, mercurial city, strange citadel of million-visaged time!—Oh! endless river and eternal rock, in which the forms of life came, passed and changed intolerably before us, and to which we came, as every youth has come, with such enormous madness, and with so mad a hope—for what?

To eat you, branch and root and tree; to devour you, golden fruit of power and love and happiness; to consume you to your sources, river and spire and rock, down to your iron roots; to entomb within our flesh forever the huge substance of your billion-footed pavements, the intolerable web and memory of dark million-visaged time.

And what is left now of all our madness, hunger, and desire? What have you given, incredible mirage of all our million shining hopes, to those who wanted to possess you wholly to your ultimate designs, your final sources, from whom you took the strength, the passion, and the innocence of youth?

What have we taken from you, protean and phantasmal shape of time? What have we remembered of your million images, of your billion weavings out of accident and number, of the mindless fury of your dateless days, the brutal stupefaction of your thousand streets and pavements? What have we seen and known that is ours forever?

Gigantic city, we have taken nothing—not even a handful of your trampled dust—we have made no image on your iron breast and left not even the print of a heel upon your stony-hearted pavements. The possession of all things, even the air we breathed, was held from us, and the river of life and time flowed through the grasp of our hands forever, and we held nothing for our hunger and desire except the proud and trembling moments, one by one. Over the trodden and forgotten words, the rust and dusty burials of yesterday, we were born again into a thousand lives and deaths, and we were left forever with only the substance of our waning flesh, and the hauntings of an accidental memory, with all its various freight of great and little things which passed and vanished instantly and could never be forgotten, and of those unbidden and unfathomed wisps and fumes of memory that share the mind with all the proud dark images of love and death.

The tugging of a leaf upon a bough in late October, a skirl of blown papers in the street, a cloud that came and went and made its shadow in the lights of April. And the forgotten laughter of lost people in dark streets, a face that passed us in another train, the house our mistress lived in as a child, a whipping flame at a slum's cold corner, the corded veins on an old man's hand, the feathery green of a tree, a daybreak in a city street in the month of May, a voice that cried out sharply and was silent in the night, and a song that a woman sang, a word that she spoke at dusk before she went away,— the memory of a ruined wall, the ancient empty visage of a half-demolished house in which love lay, the mark of a young man's fist in crumbling plaster, a lost relic, brief and temporal, in all the everlasting variousness of your life, as the madness, pain and anguish in the heart that caused it—these are all that we have taken from you, iron-breasted city, and they are ours and gone forever from us, even as things are lost and broken in the wind, and as the ghosts of time are lost, and as the everlasting river that flowed past us in darkness to the sea.

The Secret Heart of Night

OH, HE thought that he could tell her all that could be told, that youth could know, that any man had ever known about night and time and darkness, and about the city's dark and secret heart, and what lay buried in the dark and secret heart of all America. He thought that he could tell her all that any man could ever know about the huge, attentive secrecy of night, and of man's silent heart of buried, waiting, and intolerable desire, about the thing that waits there in the night-time in America, that lies buried at the city's secret heart of night, the mute and single tongue of man's intolerable desire, the silence of his single heart in all its overwhelming eloquence, the great tide flowing in the hearts of men, as dark and as mysterious as the great, unceasing river, the thing that waits and does not speak and is forever silent and that knows forever, and that has no words to say, no tongue to speak, and that unites six million celled and lonely sleepers at the heart of night and silence, in the great dark tide of the unceasing river, and of all our buried songs of hope and joy and wild desire that live forever in the heart of night and of America.

The Hudson River

THE Hudson River joins the harbor. And then the harbor joins the sea. Always the rivers run. The Hudson River drinks from out the inland slowly; it is like vats that well with purple and rich wine. The Hudson River is like purple depths of evening; it is like the flames of color on the Palisades, elves' echoes, and old Dutch and Hallowe'en. It is like the Phantom Horseman, the tossed boughs, and the demented winds, and it is like the headed cider and great fires of the Dutchmen in the winter time.

The Hudson River is like old October and tawny Indians in their camping places long ago; it is like long pipes and old tobacco; it is like cool depths and opulence; it is like the shimmer of liquid green on summer days.

The Hudson River takes the thunder of fast trains and throws a handful of lost echoes at the hills. It is like the calls of lost men in the mountains; and it is like the country boy who is coming to the city with a feeling of glory in his guts. It is like the green plush smell of the Pullman cars and snowy linen; it is like the kid in upper four and the good-looking woman down below who stirs her legs slowly in starched sheets: it is the magic river. It is like coming to the city to make money, to find glory, fame and love, and a life more fortunate and happy than any we have ever known. It is like the Knicker-bockers and early autumn; it is like the Rich Folks, and the River People, the Vanderbilts, the Astors, and the Roosevelts; it is like Robert W. Chambers and the So-ciety Folks; it is like the younger set and Hilary, and Monica, and Garth; it is like The Story Thus Far:

The lovely Monica Delavere the beautiful but spoiled daugh-ter of one of the richest men in the world meets at a party given at her father's Mount Kisco estate in honor of her ap-proaching marriage to a young architect Hilary Chedester his friend Garth Montgomery a young artist just returned from years of study abroad fascinated yet repelled by his dark passionate face and his slender hands with the longer tapering fingers of the artist and goaded by something enigmatic and mocking in his eyes in a moment of mad recklessness spurred on by a twinge of jealousy at the undue attention which she thinks Hilary is bestowing on Rita Daventry an old flame she accepts a challenge from Garth to go for a mad dash across the night in his speedster their objective being his hunting lodge in the hills and a return before dawn arrived at the lodge however Garth coolly announces that his car is out of gasoline and that he must phone for assistance to the nearest town somewhat disturbed and reflecting for the first time now on the possible scandal her reckless exploit may cause she enters the lodge now go on with the story:

[125]

"Monica's red lips curved in a smile of mocking reproof. She made a *moue*.

" 'Hardly a place I should have chosen to spend the evening, my dear man,' she said. 'But then, perhaps it is the latest Paris fashion to take ladies to deserted places and inform them you are stranded. *C'est comme ça à Paris, hein?* ' "

Yes, all these things were like the Hudson River.

And above all else, the Hudson River was like the light—oh, more than anything it was the light, the light, the tone, the texture of the magic light in which he had seen the city as a child, that made the Hudson River wonderful.

The light was golden, deep and full with all rich golden lights of harvest; the light was golden like the flesh of women, lavish as their limbs, true, depthless, tender as their glorious eyes, fine-spun and maddening as their hair, as unutterable with desire as their fragrant nests of spicery, their deep melon-heavy breasts. The light was golden like a golden morning light that shines through ancient glass into a room of old dark brown. The light was brown, dark lavish brown hued with rich lights of gold; the light was rich brown shot with gold like the sultry and exultant fragrance of ground coffee; the light was lavish brown like old stone houses gulched in morning on a city street, brown like exultant breakfast smells that come from basement areas in the brownstone houses where the rich men lived; the light was blue, steep frontal blue, like morning underneath the frontal cliff of buildings; the light was vertical cool blue, hazed with thin morning mist; the light was blue, cold flowing harbor blue of clean cool waters rimed brightly with a dancing morning gold, fresh, half-rotten with the musty river stench, blue with the blue-black of the morning gulch and canyon of the city, blue-black with cool morning shadow as the ferry, packed with its thousand small white staring faces turned one way, drove bluntly toward the rusty weathered slips.

The light was amber brown in vast dark chambers shuttered from young light where in great walnut beds the glorious women stirred in sensual warmth their lavish limbs. The light was brown-gold, like ground coffee, on merchants and the walnut houses where they lived, brown-gold like old brick buildings grimed with money and the smell of trade, brown-gold like morning on great gleaming bars of smart mahogany, the fresh wet beer-wash, lemon-rind, and the smell of angostura bitters. Then full-golden in the evening in the theatres, shining with full golden warmth and body on full golden figures of the women, on fat, red plush, and on rich, faded, slightly stale smell, and on the gilt sheaves and cupids and the cornucopias, on the fleshly, potent, softly-golden smell of all the people; and in great restaurants the light was brighter gold, but full and round like warm onyx columns, smooth warmly tinted marble, old wine in dark rounded age-encrusted bottles, and the great blonde figures of naked women on rose-clouded ceilings.

Discovery of Catawba

CATAWBA got discovered in this way: a one-eyed Spaniard, one of the early voyagers, was beating up the American coasts out of the tropics, perhaps on his way back home, perhaps only to see what could be seen. He does not tell us in the record he has left of the voyage how he happened to be there, but it seems likely that he was on his way home and had been driven off his course. Subsequent events show that he was in a very dilapidated condition, and in need of overhauling: the sails were rent, the ship was leaking, the food and water stores were almost exhausted. During the night in a storm off one of the cruelest and most evilly celebrated of the Atlantic capes, the one-eyed Spaniard was driven in and almost wrecked. By some miracle of good fortune he got through one of the inlets in the dark, and when light broke he found himself becalmed in an enormous inlet of pearl-gray water.

As the light grew he made out seawards a long almost unbroken line of sandy shoals and islands that formed a desolate barrier between the sea and the mainland, and made this bay or sound in which he found himself. Away to the west he descried now the line of the shore: it was also low, sandy, and desolate-looking. The cool gray water of morning slapped gently at the sides of his ship: he had come from the howling immensity of the sea into the desert monotony of this coast. It was as bleak and barren a coast as the one-eyed Spaniard had ever seen. And indeed, for a man who had come up so many times under the headlands of Europe, and had seen the worn escarpments of chalk, the lush greenery of the hills, and the minute striped cultivation of the earth that greet the sailor returning from a long and dangerous voyage—and awaken in him the unspeakable emotion of earth which has been tilled and used for so many centuries, with its almost personal bond for the men who have lived there on it, and whose dust is buried in it—there must have been something particularly desolate about this coast which stretched away with the immense indifference of nature into silence and wilderness. The Spaniard felt this, and the barren and desert quality of the place is duly recorded in his log, which, for the most part, is pretty dry reading.

But here a strange kind of exhilaration seizes the

Spaniard: it gets into his writing, it begins to color and pulse through the gray stuff of his record. The light of the young rising sun reddened delicately upon the waters; immense and golden it came up from the sea behind the line of the sea-dunes, and suddenly he heard the fast drumming of the wild ducks as they crossed his ship high up, flying swift and straight as projectiles. Great heavy gulls of a size and kind he had never seen before swung over his ship in vast circles, making their eerie creaking noises. The powerful birds soared on their strong even wings, with their feet tucked neatly in below their bodies; or they dove and tumbled through the air, settling to the water with great flutterings and their haunted creaking clamor: they seemed to orchestrate this desolation, they gave a tongue to loneliness and they filled the hearts of the men who had come there with a strange exultancy. For, as if some subtle and radical changes had been effected in the chemistry of their flesh and blood by the air they breathed, a kind of wild glee now possessed the one-eyed Spaniard's men. They began to laugh and sing, and to be, as he says, "marvellous merry."

During the morning the wind freshened a little; the Spaniard set his sails and stood in toward the land. By noon he was going up the coast quite near the shore, and by night he had put into the mouth of one of the coastal rivers. He took in his sails and anchored there. There was nearby on shore a settlement of "the race that inhabits these regions," and it was evident that his arrival had caused a great commotion among the inhabitants, for some who had fled away into the woods were now returning, and others were running up and down the shore, pointing and gesticulating and making a great deal of noise. But the one-eyed Spaniard had seen Indians before: that was an old story to him now, and he was not disturbed. As for his men, the strange exuberance that had seized them in the morning does not seem to have worn off, they shouted ribald jokes at the Indians, and "did laugh and caper as if they had been madde."

Nevertheless, they did not go ashore that day. The one-eyed Spaniard was worn out, and the crew was exhausted: they ate such food as they had, some raisins, cheese, and wine, and after posting a watch they went to sleep, unmindful of the fires that flickered in the Indian village, of sounds and chants and rumors, or of the forms that padded softly up and down the shore.

Then the marvellous moon moved up into the skies, and blank and full, blazed down upon the quiet waters of the sound, and upon the Indian village. It blazed upon the one-eyed Spaniard and his lonely little ship and crew, on their rich dull lamps, and on their swarthy sleeping faces; it blazed upon all the dirty richness of their ragged costumes, and on their greedy little minds, obsessed then as now by the European's greedy myth about America, to which he remains forever faithful with an unwearied and idiot pertinacity: "Where is the gold in the streets? Lead us to the emerald plantations, the diamond bushes, the plantinum mountains, and the cliffs of pearl. Brother, let us gather in the shade of the

ham and mutton trees, by the shores of ambrosial rivers:
we will bathe in the fountains of milk, and pluck hot
buttered rolls from the bread vines."

Early the next morning the Spaniard went ashore
with several of his men. "When we reached land," he
writes, "our first act was to fall down on our knees and
render thanks to God and the Blessed Virgin without
Whose intervention we had all been dead men." Their
next act was to "take possession" of this land in the
name of the King of Spain, and to ground the flag. As
we read today of this solemn ceremony, its pathos and
puny arrogance touch us with pity. For what else can
we feel for this handful of greedy adventurers "taking
possession" of the immortal wilderness in the name of
another puny fellow four thousand miles away, who
had never seen or heard of the place and could never
have understood it any better than these men? For the
earth is never "taken possession of": it possesses.

Springtime in New England

SPRING came that year like a triumph and like a prophecy—it sang and shifted like a moth of light before the youth, but he was sure that it would bring him a glory and fulfilment he had never known.

Suddenly spring came, and he felt at once exultant certainty and joy. Outside his uncle's dirty window he could see the edge of Faneuil Hall, and hear the swarming and abundant activity of the markets. The deep roar of the markets reached them across the singing and lyrical air, and he drank into his lungs a thousand proud, potent, and mysterious odors which came to him like the breath of certainty, like the proof of magic, and like the revelation that all confusion had been banished —the world that he longed for won, the word that he sought for spoken, the hunger that devoured him fed and ended. And the markets, swarming with richness, joy, and abundance, thronged below him like a living evidence of fulfilment. For it seemed to him that nowhere more than here was the passionate enigma of New England felt: New England, with its harsh and stony soil, and its tragic and lonely beauty; its desolate rocky coasts and its swarming fisheries, the white, piled, frozen bleakness of its winters with the magnificent jewelry of stars, the dark firwoods, and the warm little white houses at which it is impossible to look without thinking of groaning bins, hung bacon, hard cider, succulent bastings and love's warm, white, and opulent flesh.

There was the rustle of gingham by day and sober glances; then, under low eaves and starlight, the stir of the satiny thighs in feather beds, the white small bite and tigerish clasp of secret women—always the buried heart, the sunken passion, the frozen heat. And then, after the long, unendurably hard-locked harshness of

the frozen winter, the coming of spring as now, like a
lyrical cry, like a flicker of rain across a window glass,
like the sudden and delicate noises of a spinet—the coming of spring and ecstasy, and overnight the thrum of
wings, the burst of the tender buds, the ripple and dance
of the roughened water, the light of flowers, the sudden, fleeting, almost captured, and exultant spring.

And here, within eighty yards of the dusty little room
where his uncle Bascom had his desk, there was living
evidence that this intuition was not false: the secret
people, it was evident, did not subsist alone on codfish
and a jug full of baked beans—they ate meat, and large
chunks of it, for all day long, within the market district,
the drivers of big wagons were standing to their chins
in meat, boys dragged great baskets of raw meat along
the pavements, red-faced butchers, aproned with gouts
of blood, and wearing the battered straw hats that
butchers wear, toiled through the streets below with
great loads of loin or haunch or rib, and in chill shops
with sawdust floors the beeves were hung in frozen
regimental rows.

Right and left, around the central market, the old
buildings stretched down to the harbor and the smell of
ships: this was built-on land, in old days ships were
anchored where these cobbles were, but the warehouses
were also old—they had the musty, mellow, blackened
air and smell of the 'seventies, they looked like Victorian
prints, they reeked of ancient ledgers, of "counting
houses," of proud, monied merchants, and the soft-
spoked rumble of victorias.

and magic fulfilment that hovers like a delicate presence in the air of one of these days. Perhaps the answer is simple: perhaps it is only that this soft and sudden spring, with its darts and flicks of evanescent joy, its sprite-like presence that is only half-believed, its sound that is the sound of something lost and elfin and half-dreamed, half-heard, seems wonderful after the grim frozen tenacity of the winter, the beautiful and terrible desolation, the assault of the frost and ice on living flesh which resists it finally as it would resist the cruel battering of a brute antagonist, so that the tart, stingy speech, the tight gestures, the withdrawn and suspicious air, the thin lips, red pointed noses and hard prying eyes of these people are really the actions of those who, having to defend themselves harshly against nature, harshly defend themselves against all the world.

At any rate, the thing the boy feels who comes here at the day's end is not completion, weariness, and sterility, but a sense of swelling ecstasy, a note of brooding fulfilment. The air will have in it the wonderful odors of the market and the smell of the sea; as he walks over the bare cobbled pavement under the corrugated tin awnings of the warehouses and produce stores a hundred smells of the rich fecundity of the earth will assail him: the clean sharp pungency of thin crated wood and the citric nostalgia of oranges, lemons, and grapefruit, the stench of a decayed cabbage and the mashed pulp of a rotten orange. There will be also the warm coarse limy smell of chickens, the strong coddy smell of cold fish and oysters; and the crisp moist cleanliness of the garden smells—of great lettuces, cabbages, new potatoes, with their delicate skins loamy with sweet earth, the wonderful sweet crispness of crated celery; and then the melons—the ripe golden melons bedded in fragrant straw—and all the warm infusions of the tropics: the bananas, the pineapples and the alligator pears.

The delicate and subtle air of spring touches all these odors with a new and delicious vitality; it draws the tar out of the pavements also, and it draws slowly, subtly, from ancient warehouses, the compacted perfumes of eighty years: the sweet thin piney scents of packing-boxes, the glutinous composts of half a century, that have thickly stained old warehouse plankings, the smells of twine, tar, turpentine and hemp, and of thick mo-lasses, ginseng, pungent vines and roots and old piled sacking; the clean, ground strength of fresh coffee, brown, sultry, pungent, and exultantly fresh and clean; the smell of oats, baled hay and bran, of crated eggs and cheese and butter; and particularly the smell of meat, of frozen beeves, slick porks, and veals, of brains and livers and kidneys, of haunch, paunch, and jowl; of meat that is raw and of meat that is cooked, for up-stairs in that richly dingy block of buildings there is a room where the butchers, side by side with the bakers, the bankers, the brokers and the Harvard boys, devour thick steaks of the best and tenderest meat, smoking-hot breads, and big, jacketed potatoes.

And then there is always the sea. In dingy blocks, memoried with time and money, the buildings stretch down to the docks, and there is always the feeling that the sea was here, that this is built-on earth. A single truck will rattle over the deserted stones, and then there is the street that runs along the harbor, the dingy little clothing shops and eating places, the powerful strings of freight cars, agape and empty, odorous with their warm fatigued planking and the smells of flanges and axles that have rolled great distances.

And finally, by the edges of the water, there are great piers and storehouses, calm and potent with their finished work: they lie there, immense, starkly ugly, yet touched with the powerful beauty of enormous works and movements; they are what they are, they have been built without a flourish for the work they do, their great sides rise in level cliffs of brick, they are pierced with tracks and can engulf great rains; and now that the day is done they breathe with the vitality of a tired but living creature. A single footfall will make remote and lonely echoes in their brooding depths, there will be the expiring clatter of a single truck, the sound of a worker's voice as he says "Good-night," and then the potent and magical silence.

And then there is the sea—the sea, beautiful and mysterious as it is only when it meets the earth in harbors, the sea that bears in swell and glut of tides the odorous savor of the earth, the sea that swings and slaps against encrusted piles, the sea that is braided with long ropes of scummy weed, the sea that brings the mast and marly scent of shelled decay. There is the sea, and there are the great ships—the freighters, the fishing schooners, the clean white one-night boats that make the New York run, now also potent and silent, a glitter of bright lights, of gleaming brasses, of opulent saloons—a token of joy and splendor in dark waters, a hint of love and the velvet belly upon dark tides—and the sight of all these things, the fusion of all these odors by the sprite of May is freighted with unspeakable memories, with unutterable intuitions for the youth: he does not know what he would utter, but glory, love, power, wealth, flight and movement, and the sight of new earth in the morning, and the living corporeal fulfilment of all his ecstasy is in his wish and his conviction.

Demoniac Ecstasy

H<small>E WAS</small> liberally dowered with bright-painted gimcracks upon Christmas Day; and in his heart he hated those who advocated "useful" gifts. Gant bought him wagons, sleds, drums, horns—best of all, a small fireman's ladder wagon: it was the wonder, and finally the curse, of the neighborhood. During his unoccupied hours, he lived for months in the cellar with Harry Tarkinton and Max Isaacs: they strung the ladders on wires above the wagon, so that, at a touch, they would fall in accurate stacks. They would pretend to doze in their quarters, as firemen do, would leap to action suddenly, as one of them imitated the warning bell: "Clang-a-lang-a-lang." Then, quite beyond reason, Harry and Max yoked in a plunging team, Eugene in the driver's seat, they would leap out through the narrow door, gallop perilously to a neighbor's house, throw up ladders, open windows, effect entries, extinguish imaginary flames, and return oblivious to the shrieking indictment of the housewife.

For months they lived completely in this fantasy, modelling their actions on those of the town's firemen, and on Jannadeau, who was the assistant chief, child-proud over it: they had seen him, at the sound of the alarm, rush like a madman from his window in Gant's shop, leaving the spattered fragments of a watch upon his desk, and arriving at his duty just as the great wagon hurtled at full speed into the Square. The firemen loved to stage the most daring exhibitions before the gaping citizenry; helmeted magnificently, they hung from the wagons in gymnastic postures, one man holding another over rushing space, while number two caught in mid-air the diving heavy body of the Swiss, who deliberately risked his neck as he leaped for the rail. Thus, for one rapturous moment they stood poised triangularly over rocking speed: the spine of the town was chilled ec-statically.

And when the bells broke through the drowning winds at night, his demon rushed into his heart, bursting all cords that held him to the earth, promising him iso-lation and dominance over sea and land, inhabitation of the dark: he looked down on the whirling disk of dark forest and field, sloped over singing pines upon a huddled town, and carried its grated guarded fires against its own roofs, swerving and pouncing with his haltered storm upon their doomed and flaming walls,

Remembered Faces

THOSE faces—the secret, dark, unknown, nameless faces, the faces of the million instant casual meetings of these years, in the cars of subway trains or on the swarming streets—returned in later years to haunt him with a blazing, unforgettable intensity of vision, with an overwhelming sense of strangeness, loss and sorrow, a poignancy of familiarity, affection and regret, which was somehow, unbelievably, as wordless, grievous, full of an instant, rending and unfathomable pity, as those things a man has known best and loved with all the life and passion in him, and has lost forever—a child's quick laugh of innocence and exultant mirth, a woman's smile, an intonation in her voice, the naked, child-like look remembered in the eyes of simple, faithful people who have gone, or the snatches of the song one's brother sang when he lay drowned in darkness and delirium, as he died.

Why did the unknown faces of these years come back to him? For he could not forget the million obscure faces of those first years of his wandering when for the first time he walked alone the streets of a great city, a madman, a beggar, and a king, feeling the huge joy of the secret world impending over him with all the glory of its magic imminence, and when each furious prowl and quest into the swarming streets of life, each furious journey through the tunnel's depth was living with the intolerable prescience of triumph and discovery—a life more happy, fortunate, golden, and complete than any life before had ever been.

He did not know. He never knew why all those obscure, nameless and unknown faces of a million strangers who passed and vanished in an instant from his sight, or whom he passed a hundred times upon the streets without a word or sign of recognition, should return to haunt him later with a sense of loss, affection, and the familiarity of utter knowledge. But he knew that they came back to him in images of unfading brightness, and that the light of time, dark time, was on them all, and that there was revealed to him, in later years, something strange and mad and lonely in the lives of all of them, which he had accepted instantly, and felt no wonder or surprise at, when he had seen them.

Jewish Women

THE Jewish women were as old as nature, and as round as the earth: they had a curve in them. They had gone to the wailing walls of death and love for seven thousand years, the strong convulsive faces of the Jews were ripe with grief and wisdom, and the curve of the soul of the Jewish women was still unbroken. Female, fertile, yolky, fruitful as the earth, and ready for the plow, they offered to the famished wanderer, the alien, the exile, the baffled and infuriated man, escape and surcease of the handsome barren women, the hard varnished sawdust dolls, the arrogant and sterile women, false in look and promise as a hot-house peach, who walked the streets and had no curves or fruitfulness in them. The Jewish women waited with rich yolky cries for him, and the news they brought him, the wisdom that they gave to him was that he need not strangle like a mad dog in

a barren dark, nor perish, famished, unassuaged, within
the wilderness beside a rusted lance—but that there was
still good earth for the plow to cleave and furrow, deep
cellars for the grain, a sheath for the shining sword,
rich pockets of spiced fertility for all the maddened
lunges of desire.

They pressed around him at his table with insistent
urge, and he looked at them and saw that they were
young; and sometimes they belonged to the whole vast
family of the earth: they were like all the young people
who had ever lived—they seemed clumsy, and noisy and
good, full of hope and loyalty and folly; and sometimes again, it seemed to him that none of them had
ever known youth or innocence, that they had been
born with old and weary souls, that they were born
instructed in the huge dark history of pain, the thousand
mad and tortured sicknesses of the soul, and that the
only thirst and hunger that they knew, the desire that
drove them with an insatiate lust, was for sorrow, grief,
and human misery. Had they ever cried into the howling winds at night? Had they ever felt the sharp and
tongueless ecstasy of spring, or held their breath at
night when great wheels pounded at the rail, or trembled with a vast dark wave of pain, a wordless cry of
joy, when they heard ships calling at the harbor's mouth
and thought of new lands in the morning? Or had they
always been so old and wise, so full of grief and evil?

The girls pressed in on him their sensual wave, and
the boys stood farther off, behind them, waiting, and he
saw the dark and furtive glances of the men pass slyly,

each to each, in swift final looks of cynical communication. They waited for the women to have done, with a kind of hard and weary patience, an old and knowing agreement, a sense of acceptance, as if they had known for thousands of years that their women would betray them with a Gentile lover, and yet with a kind of triumph, as if they also knew they would regain them and be victorious in the end.

They seemed to have gained from life the terrible patience, the old and crafty skill and caution that come from long enduring of pain: as he looked at them he knew that they would never be wild and drunken, or beat their knuckles bloody on a wall, or lie beaten and senseless in the stews, but he knew that with smooth faces they would decant the bottle for some man who did, and that they would read him quietly to his desperate fate with their dark, mocking, and insatiate eyes. They had learned that a savage word would break no bones and that the wound of betrayal or a misprized love is less fatal than the stroke of the sword, the thrust of the knife: in the years that followed he saw that physically they were, for the most part, incorrupt, old and cautious, filled with skill and safety—that they had lived so long and grown so wise and crafty that their subtile, million-noted minds could do without and hold in dark contempt the clumsy imperfections of a fleshly evil—that they could evoke and live completely in a world of cruel and subtle intuitions, unphrased and un-utterable intensities of cruelty, shame, and horror, without lifting a finger or turning a hand. Thus, in these years, as his own mind grew mad and twisted with the insane fabrications of a poisonous jealousy—as it immediately and without a bridge or break translated into terms of literal physical actuality an insane picture of cruelty and horror: of daughters who acted as procurers to their mothers, of sons and husbands going unperturbed to sleep in houses where their sisters, wives, and children lay quilted in the lust and evil abominations of an adulterous love, of calm untelling faces, looks and glances of a childlike purity, an air of goodness, faith and morning innocence throughout, while the whole knowledge of an unspeakable evil trembled in their hearts forever with an obscene and soundless laughter— these abominations of his fancy, this vile progeny which his mad brain translated into literal fact, were probably for the most part only images the cruel and subtile minds of the old, wise, patient Jews had evoked and played with in their complex fantasy; and as he looked at the swarm of dark insistent faces round him at the table, an overwhelming sensation of defeat and desolation drowned his spirit—their dark looks read, and ate, and mocked at him, and yet were full of affection and tenderness as if they loved the food they fed upon: it seemed to him that he alone must die; that he must break his heart and smash his bones, lie beaten, drunken, mashed and senseless in the dives, must wreck his reason, lose his sanity, destroy his talent, and die a mad-dog howling in the wilderness while they—they alone—these old, wise, weary, patient, pain-devouring, subtile-minded Jews—endured.

The Inevitable Instant

As Eugene watched, the old fatality of place returned. Each day, he thought, we pass the spot where some day we must die; or shall I, too, ride dead to some mean building yet unknown? Shall this bright clay, the hill-bound, die in lodgings yet unbuilt? Shall these eyes, drenched with visions yet unseen, stored with the viscous and interminable seas at dawn, with the sad comfort of unfulfilled Arcadias, seal up their cold dead dreams upon a tick, as this, in time, in some hot village of the plains?

He caught and fixed the instant. A telegraph messenger wheeled vigorously in from the avenue with pumping feet, curved widely into the alley at his right, jerking his wheel up sharply as he took the curb, and coasted down to the delivery boy's entrance. And post o'er land and ocean without rest. Milton, thou should'st be living at this hour.

The World of First Light

AMONG the dreams that returned to haunt his
waking, watchful sleep during the strange,
living vision of that green spring, as he lay
hearted at the pulse of time, there was one
which remained ever after in his memory.

He was striding along a wide and sandy beach and
by the side of a calm and tranquilly flowing sea. The
waves broke quietly and evenly in a long, low roll upon
the beach, rushing up the sand in small hissing eddies
of foam and water. Below his feet the firm, brown sand
sprang back with an elastic vitality, a warm and vital
wind was blowing, and he drew into his lungs exultantly
the smell of the sea, and of the warm, wet, fragrant
beach, ribbed evenly with braided edges of brown sea-
weed.

He did not recognize the scene as one which he had

ever visited before, and yet he felt an instant and complete familiarity with it, as if he had known it forever. Behind him, drumming evenly upon the hard, elastic sand, and fading away into the distance with a hard, wooden thunder of wheels, he heard the furious rhythm of pounding hooves of driven horses. He knew that he had just descended from a ship, and that he was living in one of the antique and early ages of the earth; and all of this he knew with joy and wonder, and without surprise, with the thrill of recovering something he had always known and had lost forever.

It was a scene out of the classic period of the earth, and yet it was wholly different from every image he had ever had about this earth, in his imagination. For where, in every vision of his mind and reading, that earth had come to him in a few sharp and radiant colors, in a structure of life as glowing and proportionate as one of its faultless temples, as remote from the world he lived in as all its fables, myths, and legends, this earth he now walked on was permeated with the living tones and weathers of life.

The world of Homer was the world of first light, sunlight, and of morning: the sea was wine-dark, a gold and sapphire purity of light fell on the walls of Troy, a lucent depthless purity of light welled from the eyes of Helen, as false, fatal, and innocently corrupt a woman as ever wrought destruction on the earth. The light that fell on Nausicaa and her maidens was all gold and crystal like the stream they bathed in, as lucent in purity as their limbs, as radiant as joy and morning on the earth; and even the lights of vengeance and the rout of the dread furies that fell upon the doomed and driven figure of Orestes were as fatal as blood, as relentless as an antique tragedy, as toneless as a destiny.

And in his pictures of a later time, of Athens in the period of recorded history, of Pericles and Plato and the time of the wars with Sparta, the scenes of history were bathed in these radiant and perfect lights and weathers. He knew these men were made of living, breathing flesh and subject to the errors and imperfections of mortal men, and yet when he tried to think of a slum in Athens, of people with bad teeth, blemished skins, muddy complexions—of disease, filth, and squalor among them, and of the million weary, beaten, dusty, sweating moments of their lives, he could not. Even human grief, pain, and trouble took on a color of classical perfection, of tragic grandeur, and the tortured and distressful skein of human life, with all that is ugly, trivial, and disgusting in it, took on the logical pattern of design and ordered destiny.

The light that fell upon them was of gold and sapphire, and of singing, or as ominous and fatal as a certain and inexorable doom; but now he walked this beach in one of the classical periods of the earth, and nothing was as he had tried to picture it, and yet all was as familiar as if he had known it forever.

There was no gold nor sapphire in the air: it was warm and sultry, omened with some troubling, variable and exultant menace, fraught with the sulphurous promise of a storm, pregnant with mystery and discovery, touched with a hundred disturbing elements and weathers of man's soul, and scented with a thousand warm and spermy odors of the land and sea, that touched man's entrails with delight and prophecy.

And the sea also was neither lyrical with gold and blue, nor wine-dark in its single harmony: the sea was dark and sultry as the sky that bent above it; murked greedily, thickly, milkily, as it rolled quietly and broke upon the beach; as omened with impalpable prophecy as the earth and air.

He did not know the reason for his being there, and yet he knew beyond a doubt that he had come there for a purpose, that some one was waiting for him there, that the greatest joy and triumph he had ever known was impending in this glorious meeting.

October Has Come Again

OCTOBER had come again, and that year it was
sharp and soon: frost was early, burning the
thick green on the mountain sides to massed
brilliant hues of blazing colors, painting the
air with sharpness, sorrow and delight—and with Oc-

tober. Sometimes, and often, there was warmth by day, an ancient drowsy light, a golden warmth and pollenated haze in afternoon, but over all the earth there was the premonitory breath of frost, an exultancy for all the men who were returning, a haunting sorrow for the buried men, and for all those who were gone and would not come again.

His father was dead, and now it seemed to him that he had never found him. His father was dead, and yet he sought him everywhere, and could not believe that he was dead, and was sure that he would find him. It was October and that year, after years of absence and of wandering, he had come home again.

He could not think that his father had died, but he had come home in October, and all the life that he had known there was strange and sorrowful as dreams. And yet he saw it all in shapes of deathless brightness—the town, the streets, the magic hills, and the plain prognathous faces of the people he had known. He saw them all in shapes of deathless brightness, and everything was instantly familiar as his father's face, and stranger, more phantasmal than a dream.

Their words came to him with the accents of an utter naturalness, and yet were sorrowful and lost and strange like voices speaking in a dream, and in their eyes he read a lost and lonely light, as if they were all phantoms and all lost, or as if he had revisited the shores of this great earth again with a heart of fire, a cry of pain and ecstasy, a memory of intolerable longing and regret for all the glorious and exultant life

that he had known and which he must visit now forever as a fleshless ghost, never to touch, to hold, to
have its palpable warmth and substance for his own
again. He had come home again, and yet he could not
believe his father was dead, and he thought he heard
his great voice ringing in the street again, and that he
would see him striding toward him across the Square
with his gaunt earth-devouring stride, or find him
waiting every time he turned the corner, or lunging toward the house bearing the tremendous provender of
his food and meat, bringing to them all the deathless
security of his strength and power and passion, bringing to them all again the roaring message of his fires
that shook the fire-full chimney throat with their terrific
blast, giving to them all again the exultant knowledge
that the good days, the magic days, the golden weather
of their lives would come again, and that this dream-
like and phantasmal world in which they found themselves would waken instantly, as it had once, to all the
palpable warmth and glory of the earth, if only his
father would come back to make it live, to give them
life, again.

Therefore, he could not think that he was dead, and
yet it was October, and that year he had come home
again. And at night, in his mother's house, he would lie
in his bed in the dark, hearing the wind that rattled
dry leaves along the empty pavement, hearing far-
off across the wind, the barking of a dog, feeling dark
time, strange time, dark secret time, as it flowed on
around him, remembering his life, this house, and all

[158]

the million strange and secret visages of time, dark time, thinking, feeling, thinking:

"October has come again, has come again. . . . I have come home again, and found my father dead . . . and that was time . . . time . . . time . . . Where shall I go now? What shall I do now? For October has come again, but there has gone some richness from the life we knew, and we are lost."

Storm shook the house at night—the old house, his mother's house—where he had seen his brother die. The old doors swung and creaked in darkness, darkness pressed against the house, the darkness filled them, filled the house at night, it moved about them soft and secret, palpable, filled with a thousand secret presences of sorrowful time and memory, moving about him as he lay below his brother's room in darkness, while storm shook the house in late October, and something creaked and rattled in the wind's strong blast. It was October, and he had come home again: he could not believe that his father was dead.

Wind beat at them with burly shoulders in the night. The darkness moved there in the house like something silent, palpable—a spirit breathing in his mother's house, a demon and a friend—speaking to him its silent and intolerable prophecy of flight, of darkness and the storm, moving about him constantly, prowling about the edges of his life, ever beside him, with him, in him, whispering:

"Child, child—come with me—come with me to your brother's grave tonight. Come with me to the places where the young men lie whose bodies have long since been buried in the earth. Come with me where they walk and move again tonight, and you shall see your brother's face again, and hear his voice, and see again, as they march toward you from their graves, the company of the young men who died, as he did, in October, speaking to you their messages of flight, of triumph, and the all-exultant darkness, telling you that all will be again as it was once."

October had come again, and he would lie there in his mother's house at night, and feel the darkness moving softly all about him, and hear the dry leaves scampering on the street outside, and the huge and burly rushes of the wind. And then the wind would rush away with huge caprice, and he could hear it far off roaring with remote demented cries in the embraces of great trees, and he would lie there thinking:

"October has come again—has come again"—feeling the dark around him, not believing that his father could be dead, thinking: "The strange and lonely years have come again. . . . I have come home again . . . come home again . . . and will it not be with us all as it has been?"—feeling the darkness as it moved about him, thinking, "Is it not the same darkness that I knew in childhood, and have I not lain here in bed before, and felt this darkness moving all about me? . . . Did we not hear dogs that barked in darkness, in October?" he then thought. "Were not their howls far broken by the wind? . . . And hear dry leaves that scampered on the streets at night . . . and the huge and burly rushes of the wind . . . and hear huge limbs that stiffly creak in the remote demented howlings of the burly wind . . . and something creaking in the wind at night . . . and think, then, as we think now, of all the men who have gone and never will come back again, and of our friends and brothers who lie buried in the earth? . . . Oh, has not October now come back again?" he cried. "As always—as it always was?"—and hearing the great darkness softly prowling in his mother's house at night, and thinking, feeling, thinking, as he lay there in the dark:

"Now October has come again which in our land is different from October in the other lands. The ripe, the golden month has come again, and in Virginia the chinkapins are falling. Frost sharps the middle music of the seasons, and all things living on the earth turn home again. The country is so big you cannot say the country has the same October. In Maine, the frost comes sharp and quick as driven nails, just for a week or so the woods, all of the bright and bitter leaves, flare up: the maples turn a blazing bitter red, and other leaves turn yellow like a living light, falling about you as you walk the woods, falling about you like small pieces of the sun so that you cannot say where sunlight shakes and flutters on the ground, and where the leaves.

"Meanwhile the Palisades are melting in massed molten colors, the season swings along the nation, and a little later in the South dense woodings on the hill begin to glow and soften, and when they smell the burning wood-smoke in Ohio children say: 'I'll bet that there's a forest fire in Michigan.' And the mountaineer goes hunting down in North Carolina, he stays out late with mournful flop-eared hounds, a rind of moon comes up across the rude lift of the hills: what do his friends say to him when he stays out late? Full of hoarse innocence and laughter, they will say: 'Mister, yore ole woman's goin' to whup ye if ye don't go home.' "

Oh, return, return!

"October is the richest of the seasons: the fields are cut, the granaries are full, the bins are loaded to the brim with fatness, and from the cider-press the rich brown oozings of the York Imperials run. The bee bores to the belly of the yellowed grape, the fly gets old and fat and blue, he buzzes loud, crawls slow, creeps heavily to death on sill and ceiling, the sun goes down in blood and pollen across the bronzed and mown fields of old October.

"The corn is shocked: it sticks out in hard yellow rows upon dried ears, fit now for great red barns in Pennsylvania, and the big stained teeth of crunching horses. The indolent hooves kick swiftly at the boards, the barn is sweet with hay and leather, wood and apples —this, and the clean dry crunching of the teeth is all: the sweat, the labor, and the plow is over. The late pears mellow on a sunny shelf; smoked hams hang to the warped barn rafters; the pantry shelves are loaded with 300 jars of fruit. Meanwhile the leaves are turning, turning, up in Maine the chestnut burrs plop thickly to the earth in gusts of wind, and in Virginia the chinkapins are falling.

"There is a smell of burning in small towns in afternoon, and men with buckles on their arms are raking leaves in yards as boys come by with straps slung back across their shoulders. The oak leaves, big and brown, are bedded deep in yard and gutter: they make deep wadings to the knee for children in the streets. The fire will snap and crackle like a whip, sharp acrid smoke will sting the eyes, in mown fields the little vipers of the flame eat past the black coarse edges of burned stubble like a line of locusts. Fire drives a thorn of memory in the heart.

"The bladed grass, a forest of small spears of ice, is thawed by noon: summer is over but the sun is warm again, and there are days throughout the land, of gold and russet. But summer is dead and gone, the earth is waiting, suspense and ecstasy are gnawing at the hearts of men, the brooding prescience of frost is there. The sun flames red and bloody as it sets, there are old red glintings on the battered pails, the great barn gets the ancient light as the boy slops homeward with warm foaming milk. Great shadows lengthen in the fields, the old red light dies swiftly, and the sunset barking of the hounds is faint and far and full of frost: there are shrewd whistles to the dogs, and frost and silence— this is all. Wind stirs and scuffs and rattles up the old brown leaves, and through the night the great oak leaves keep falling.

"Trains cross the continent in a swirl of dust and thunder, the leaves fly down the tracks behind them: the great trains cleave through gulch and gully, they rumble with spoked thunder on the bridges over the powerful brown wash of mighty rivers, they toil through hills, they skirt the rough brown stubble of shorn fields, they whip past empty stations in the little towns and their great stride pounds its even pulse across America. Field and hill and lift and gulch and hollow, mountain and plain and river, a wilderness with fallen trees across it, a thicket of bedded brown and twisted undergrowth, a plain, a desert, and a plantation, a mighty landscape with no fenced niceness, an immensity of fold and convolution that can never be remembered, that can never be forgotten, that has never been described—weary with harvest, potent with every fruit and ore, the immeasurable richness enbrowned with autumn, rank, crude, unharnessed, careless of scars or beauty, everlasting and magnificent, a cry, a space, an ecstasy!—American earth in old October.

"And the great winds howl and swoop across the land: they make a distant roaring in great trees, and boys in bed will stir in ecstasy, thinking of demons and vast swoopings through the earth. All through the night there is the clean, the bitter rain of acorns, and the chestnut burrs are plopping to the ground.

"And often in the night there is only the living silence, the distant frosty barking of a dog, the small clumsy stir and feathery stumble of the chickens on limed roosts, and the moon, the low and heavy moon of autumn, now barred behind the leafless poles of pines, now at the pinewoods' brooding edge and summit, now falling with ghost's dawn of milky light upon rimed clods of fields and on the frosty scurf on pumpkins, now whiter, smaller, brighter, hanging against the steeple's slope, hanging the same way in a million streets, steeping all the earth in frost and silence.

"Then a chime of frost-cold bells may peal out on the brooding air, and people lying in their beds will listen. They will not speak or stir, silence will gnaw the darkness like a rat, but they will whisper in their hearts:

" 'Summer has come and gone, has come and gone. And now—?' But they will say no more, they will have no more to say: they will wait listening, silent and brooding as the frost, to time, strange ticking time, dark time that haunts us with the briefness of our days. They will think of men long dead, of men now buried in the earth, of frost and silence long ago, of a forgotten face and moment of lost time, and they will think of things they have no words to utter.

"And in the night, in the dark, in the living sleeping silence of the towns, the million streets, they will hear the thunder of the fast express, the whistles of great ships upon the river.

"What will they say then? What will they say?"

Only the darkness moved about him as he lay there thinking, feeling in the darkness: a door creaked softly in the house.

"October is the season for returning: the bowels of youth are yearning with lost love. Their mouths are dry and bitter with desire: their hearts are torn with the thorns of spring. For lovely April, cruel and flowerful,

[165]

will tear them with sharp joy and wordless lust. Spring has no language but a cry; but crueller than April is the asp of time.

"October is the season for returning: even the town is born anew," he thought. "The tide of life is at the full again, the rich return to business or to fashion, and the bodies of the poor are rescued out of heat and weariness. The ruin and horror of the summer are forgotten—a memory of hot cells and humid walls, a hell of ugly sweat and labor and distress and hopelessness, a limbo of pale greasy faces. Now joy and hope have revived again in the hearts of millions of people, they breathe the air again with hunger, their movements are full of life and energy. The mark of their summer's suffering is still legible upon their flesh, there is something starved and patient in their eyes, and a look that has a child's hope and expectation in it.

"All things on earth point home in old October: sailors to sea, travellers to walls and fences, hunters to field and hollow and the long voice of the hounds, the lover to the love he has forsaken—all things that live upon this earth return, return: Father, will you not, too, come back again?

"Where are you now, when all things on the earth come back again? For have not all these things been here before, have we not seen them, heard them, known them, and will they not live again for us as they did once, if only you come back again?

"Father, in the night time, in the dark, I have heard the thunder of the fast express. In the night, in the dark,

I have heard the howling of the winds among great trees, and the sharp and windy raining of the acorns. In the night, in the dark, I have heard the feet of rain upon the roofs, the glut and gurgle of the gutter-spouts, and the soaking gulping throat of all the mighty earth, drinking its thirst out in the month of May—and heard the sorrowful silence of the river in October. The hillstreams foam and welter in a steady plunge, the mined clay drops and melts and eddies in the night, the snake coils cool and glistening under dripping ferns, the water roars down past the mill in one sheer sheetlike plunge, making a steady noise like wind, and in the night, in the dark, the river flows by us to the sea.

"The great maw slowly drinks the land as we lie sleeping: the mined banks cave and crumble in the dark, the earth melts and drops into its tide, great horns are baying in the gulph of night, great boats are baying at the river's mouth. Thus, darkened by our dumpings, thickened by our stains, rich, rank, beautiful, and unending as all life, all living, the river, the dark immortal river, full of strange tragic time, is flowing by us—by us—by us—to the sea.

"All this has been upon the earth, and will abide forever. But you are gone; our lives are ruined and broken in the night, our lives are mined below us by the river, our lives are whirled away into the sea and darkness, and we are lost unless you come to give us life again.

"Come to us, Father, in the watches of the night, come to us as you always came, bringing to us the invincible sustenance of your strength, the limitless treasure of your bounty, the tremendous structure of your life that will shape all lost and broken things on earth again into a golden pattern of exultancy and joy. Come to us, Father, while the winds howl in the darkness, for October has come again bringing with it huge prophecies of death and life and the great cargo of the men who will return. For we are ruined, lost, and broken if you do not come, and our lives, like rotten chips, are whirled about us onward in darkness to the sea."

So, thinking, feeling, speaking, he lay there in his mother's house, but there was nothing in the house but silence and the moving darkness: storm shook the house and huge winds rushed upon them, and he knew then that his father would not come again, and that all the life that he had known was now lost and broken as a dream.

Light of Fading Day

AND the slant light steepened in the skies, the old red light of waning day made magic fire upon the river, and the train made on forever its tremendous monotone that was like silence and forever—and now there was nothing but that tremendous monotone of time and silence and the river, the haunted river, the enchanted river that drank forever its great soundless tides from out the inland slowly, and that moved through all men's lives the magic thread of its huge haunting spell, and that linked his life to magic kingdoms and to lotus-land and to all the vision of the magic earth that he had dreamed of as a child, and that bore him on forever out of magic to all the grime and sweat and violence of the city, the unceasing city, the million-footed city, and into America.

The great river burned there in his vision in that light of fading day and it was hung there in that spell of silence and forever, and it was flowing on forever, and it was stranger than a legend, and as dark as time.

The Sound of the Sea

H E WAS like a man who had died, and had been re-born. All that had gone before lived in a ghostly world. He thought of his family, of Ben, of Laura James, as if they were ghosts. The world itself turned ghost. All through that month of August, while the war marched to its ending, he looked upon its dying carnival. Nothing seemed any longer hard and hot and raw and new. Everything was old. Everything was dying. A vast aerial music, forever far-faint, like the language of his forgotten world, sounded in his ears. He had known birth. He had known pain and love. He had known hunger. Almost he had known death.

At night, when he was not called back for work he rode out by trolley to one of the Virginia beaches. But the only sound that was real, that was near and present, was the sound in his heart, in his brain, of the everlasting sea. He turned his face toward it: behind him, the cheap million lights of the concessionaires, the clatter, the racket, the confetti, the shrill blare of the saxophones, all the harsh joyless noise of his country, was softened, was made sad, far, and phantom. The wheeling merry-go-round, the blaring dance-orchestra, played *K-K-K-Katy, Beautiful Katy, Poor Little Buttercup,* and *Just a Baby's Prayer at Twilight.*

And that cheap music turned elfin and lovely: it was mixed into magic—it became a part of the romantic and lovely Virginias, of the surge of the sea as it rolled in from the eternal dark, across the beach, and of his own magnificent sorrow—his triumphant loneliness after pain and love and hunger.

His face was thin and bright as a blade, below the great curling shock of his hair; his body as lean as a starved cat's; his eyes bright and fierce.

O sea! (he thought) I am the hill-born, the prison-pent, the ghost, the stranger, and I walk here at your side. O sea, I am lonely like you, I am strange and far like you, I am sorrowful like you; my brain, my heart, my life, like yours, have touched strange shores. You are like a woman lying below yourself on the coral floor. You are an immense and fruitful woman with vast thighs and a great thick mop of curling woman's hair floating like green moss above your belly. And you will bring me to the happy land, you will wash me to glory in bright ships.

There by the sea of the dark Virginias, he thought of

the forgotten faces, of all the million patterns of himself, the ghost of his lost flesh. The child that heard Swain's cow, the lost boy in the Ozarks, the carrier of news among the blacks, and the boy who went in by the lattice with Jim Trivett. And the waitress, and Ben, and Laura? Dead, too? Where? How? Why? Why has the web been woven? Why do we die so many deaths? How came I here beside the sea? O lost, O far and lonely, where?

figure waned and wasted under the ravages of the
cancer that was consuming him until he had become
only the enfeebled shadow of his former self, his gaunt
hands, on which there was so little which death could
consume, lost none of their former rock-like heaviness,
strength and shapely power. Thus, even when the giant
figure of the man had become nothing but a spectral
remnant of itself, sunk in a sorrow of time, awaiting
death, those great, still-living hands of power and
strength hung incredibly, horribly, from that spectral
form of death to which they were attached.

And for this reason those powerful hands of life
evoked, as nothing else could have done, in an instant
searing flash of memory and recognition, the lost world
of his father's life of manual power, hunger, fury, savage abundance and wild joy, the whole enchanted structure of that lost life of magic he had made for them.
Constantly, those great hands of life joined, with an
almost grotesque incongruity, to that scarecrow form of
wasting death would awake for them, as nothing else
on earth could do, all of the sorrowful ghosts of time,
the dream-like spell and terror of the years between,
the years of phantom death, the horror of unreality,
strangeness, disbelief, and memory, that haunted them.

So was it now, even in death, with his father's hands.
In their powerful, gaunt and shapely clasp, as he lay
dead in his coffin, there seemed to be held and gathered,
somehow, all of his life that could never die—a living
image of the essential quality of his whole life with its
fury and unrest, desire and hunger, the tremendous

sweep and relish of its enormous appetites and the huge endowment of its physical and sensual powers.

Thus, one could suppose that on the face of a dead poet there might remain—how, where or in what way we could not tell—a kind of flame, a light, a glory, the magic and still living chrysm of his genius. And on the face of the dead conqueror we might still see living, arrogant, and proud with all its dark authorities the frown of power, the inflexible tyranny of stern command, the special infinitude of the invincible will that would not die with life, and that incredibly remains, still dark and living in its scorn and mockery of time.

Then, on the face of an old dead prophet or philosopher there would live and would not die the immortality of proud, lonely thought. We could not say just where that spirit rested. Sometimes it would seem to rest upon the temples of the grand and lonely head. Sometimes we would think it was a kind of darkness in the shadows of the closed and sunken eyes, sometimes the marsh fire of a dark and lambent flame that hovered round the face, that could never be fixed, but that we always knew was there.

And just as poet, prophet, priest and conqueror might each retain in death some living and fitting image of his whole life's truth, so would the strength, the skill, all of the hope, hunger, fury, and unrest that had lashed and driven on through life the gaunt figure of a stonecutter, be marvellously preserved in the granite power and symmetry of those undying hands.

Night

IT WAS sunset. The sun's vast rim, blood-red, rested upon the western earth, in a great field of murky pollen. It sank beyond the western ranges. The clear sweet air was washed with gold and pearl. The vast hills melted into purple solitudes: they were like Canaan and rich grapes. The motors of cove people toiled up around the horse-shoe of the road. Dusk came. The bright twinkling lights in the town went up. Darkness melted over the town like dew: it washed out all the day's distress, the harsh confusions. Low wailing sounds came faintly up from Niggertown.

And above him the proud stars flashed into heaven: there was one, so rich and low, that he could have picked it, if he had climbed the hill beyond the Jew's great house. One, like a lamp, hung low above the heads of men returning home. (O Hesperus, you bring us all good things). One had flashed out the light that winked on him the night that Ruth lay at the feet of Boaz; and one on Queen Isolt; and one on Corinth and on Troy. It was night, vast brooding night, the mother of loneliness, that washes our stains away. He was washed in the great river of night, in the Ganges tides of redemption.

His bitter wound was for the moment healed in him:
he turned his face upward to the proud and tender
stars, which made him a god and a grain of dust, the
brother of eternal beauty and the son of death—alone,
alone.

Hymn to Death, Loneliness and Sleep

THEREFORE, immortal fellowship, proud Death, stern Loneliness, and Sleep, dear friends in whose communion I shall live forever, out of the passion and the substance of my life I have made this praise for you:

To you, proud Death, who sit so grandly on the brows of little men—first to you! Proud Death, proud Death, whom I have seen by darkness, at so many times, and always when you came to nameless men, what have you ever touched that you have not touched with love and pity, Death? Proud Death, wherever we have seen your face, you came with mercy, love, and pity, Death, and brought to all of us your compassionate sentences of pardon and release. For have you not retrieved from exile the desperate lives of men who never found their

home? Have you not opened your dark door for us
who never yet found doors to enter, and given us a room
who, roomless, doorless, unassuaged, were driven on
forever through the streets of life? Have you not offered
us your stern provender, Death, with which to stay the
hunger that grew to madness from the food it fed upon,
and given all of us the goal for which we sought but
never found, the certitude, the peace, for which our
over-laden hearts contended, and made for us, in your
dark house, an end of all the tortured wandering and
unrest that lashed us on forever? Proud Death, proud
Death, not for the glory that you added to the glory of
the king, proud Death, nor for the honor you imposed
upon the dignities of famous men, proud Death, nor
for the final magic you have given to the lips of genius,
Death, but because you come so gloriously to us who
never yet knew glory, so proudly and sublimely to us
whose lives were nameless and obscure, because you
give to all of us—the nameless, faceless, voiceless atoms
of the earth—the awful chrysm of your grandeur, Death,
because I have seen and known you so well, and have
lived alone so long with Loneliness, your brother, I do
not fear you any longer, friend, and I have made this
praise for you.

Now, Loneliness forever and the earth again! Dark
brother and stern friend, immortal face of darkness and
of night, with whom the half part of my life was spent,
and with whom I shall abide now till my death forever,
what is there for me to fear as long as you are with me?
Heroic friend, blood-brother of proud Death, dark face,

have we not gone together down a million streets, have we not coursed together the great and furious avenues of night, have we not crossed the stormy seas alone, and known strange lands, and come again to walk the continent of night, and listen to the silence of the earth? Have we not been brave and glorious when we were together, friend, have we not known triumph, joy, and glory on this earth—and will it not be again with me as it was then, if you come back to me? Come to me, brother, in the watches of the night, come to me in the secret and most silent heart of darkness, come to me as you always came, bringing to me once more the old invincible strength, the deathless hope, the triumphant joy and confidence that will storm the ramparts of the earth again.

Come to me through the fields of night, dear friend, come to me with the horses of your sister, Sleep, and we shall listen to the silence of the earth and darkness once again, we shall listen to the heartbeats of the sleeping men, as with soft and rushing thunder of their hooves the strange dark horses of great Sleep come on again.

They come! Ships call! The hooves of night, the horses of great Sleep, are coming on below their manes of darkness. And forever the rivers run. Deep as the tides of Sleep the rivers run. We call!

They come: my great dark horses come! With soft and rushing thunder of their hooves they come, and the horses of Sleep are galloping, galloping over the land.

Oh, softly, softly the great dark horses of Sleep are

galloping over the land. The great black bats are flying over us. The tides of Sleep are moving through the nation; beneath the tides of Sleep and time strange fish are moving.

For Sleep has crossed the worn visages of day, and in the night-time, in the dark, in all the sleeping silence of the towns, the faces of ten million men are strange and dark as time. In Sleep we lie all naked and alone, in Sleep we are united at the heart of night and darkness, and we are strange and beautiful asleep; for we are dying in the darkness, and we know no death, there is no death, there is no life, no joy, no sorrow and no glory on the earth but Sleep.

Come, mild and magnificent Sleep, and let your tides flow through the nation. O daughter of unmemoried desire, sister of Death, and my stern comrade, Loneliness, bringer of peace and dark forgetfulness, healer and redeemer, dear enchantress, hear us: come to us through the fields of night, over the plains and rivers of the everlasting earth, bringing to the huge vexed substance of this world and to all the fury, pain, and madness of our lives the merciful anodyne of your redemption. Seal up the porches of our memory, tenderly, gently, steal our lives away from us, blot out the vision of lost love, lost days, and all our ancient hungers; great Transformer, heal us!

Oh, softly, softly, the great dark horses of Sleep are galloping over the land. The tides of Sleep are moving in the hearts of men, they flow like rivers in the night, they flow with glut and fullness of their dark un-

fathomed strength into a million pockets of the land
and over the shores of the whole earth. They flow with
the full might of their advancing and inexorable flood
across the continent of night, across the breadth and
sweep of the immortal earth, until the hearts of all men
living are relieved of their harsh weight, the souls of all
men who have ever drawn in the breath of anguish and
of labor are healed, assuaged, and conquered by the vast
enchantments of dark, silent, all-engulfing Sleep.

Sleep falls like silence on the earth, it fills the hearts
of ninety million men, it moves like magic in the mountains, and walks like night and darkness across the
plains and rivers of the earth, until low upon lowlands,
and high upon hills, flows gently sleep, smooth-sliding
sleep—oh, sleep—sleep—sleep!

Far Away Lay America

THEIR names were Octave Feuillet, Alfred Capus, and Maurice Donnay; their names were Hermant, Courteline, and René Bazin; their names were Jules Renard, Marcelle Tinayre, and André Theuriet; and Clarétie, and Frapié and Tristan Bernard; and de Régnier and Paul Reboux, and Lavedan; their names were Rosny, Gyp, Boylesve, and Richepin; their names were Bordeaux, Prévost, Margueritte, and Duvernois—their names, Great God, their names were countless as the sands upon the shore —and in the end, their names were only names and names and names—and nothing more.

Or, if their names were something more than names —if they sometimes shaped themselves in his mind as personalities—these personalities were faded, graceful, and phantasmal ones—each talented and secure in his position, and curiously alike—each brave and good and gentle in his trade, like lesser-known knights of the Round Table. He knew that few of them had been the hero of a generation, the leader of a century; he knew that none of them had rivalled Balzac, surpassed Stendhal, out-done Flaubert. And for this reason, their vague, phantasmal company became more haunting-strange to him than if they had.

He knew, as well, that there must be among them great differences of talent, great differences of style. His reason told him that some were good, and some were fair, and some were only cheap; even his meagre understanding of their tongue showed him that there was a great range, every kind of difference in their choice and treatment of a subject—a range that swept from the gracefully ironic sentiment of *Les Vacances d'un Jeune Homme Sage* to the stern earth-and-peasant austerity of *Le Blé qui lève;* from the dream nostalgia of *Le Passé Vivant* to the salty and difficult drolleries of *Messieurs les Ronds-de-Cuir* or *Le Train de 8h 47.*

He knew that each of these men must have had his own style, his special quality which would instantly be discerned and appraised by a French reader—he knew that some had written of the quiet life of the provinces, and that others wrote of the intrigue, the love affairs, the worldly and sophisticated gentry, of Paris; he knew that some were writers of a graceful sentiment, some delicately ironic, some drolly comic, some savagely satiric, and some grimly tragic.

But all of them seemed to come from the same place, to have the same quality, to evoke the same perfume. They were the vague and shadowy figures of a charming, beautiful, and legendary kind of life—a life that was all the more legendary to him because he was constantly groping with half-meanings, filling in his faulty understanding of the language with painful intuitions, tearing desperately at the contents of unnumbered volumes, with a tortured hunger of frustration, an aching brain, a dictionary in one hand, and one of these slick and flimsy little volumes in another.

And for this reason, perhaps, as much as any other— because of this savage struggle with an alien tongue, this agonizing, half-intuitive effort by which he groped his way to understanding through a book—the books themselves, and these graceful and shadowy figures who produced them, took on a quality that was as strange as the whole experience of these first weeks in Paris had become. Indeed, in later years, the legendary quality of his savage conflict with this world of print became

indistinguishably mixed with the legendary quality of
the life around him. Perhaps, even the swift, graceful,
and fascinating little drawings and illustrations which
dotted the pages of these books were in some measure
responsible for this illusion: the pictures gave to the
hard and difficult pages of a thousand fictions the illusion of an actual reality: in these little pictures he could
see and recognize a thousand things that had already
grown familiar to him—the narrow sidewalks and the
tall and ancient houses of the Latin Quarter, the bridges
of the Seine, the interior of a railway compartment, the
great grilled gate of a château, people sitting at the
tables in a café or on the terrace, the walls, the roofs,
the chimney-pots of Paris which, no matter what
changes had come about in human costume, feminine
fashions, top-hats, frock-coats, or facial whiskerage,
had themselves changed very little.

The most extraordinary and vividly imagined phe-
nomenon of his desperate struggle to understand these
innumerable fictions was this: Although his reason told
him that all these men—all these phantasmal and haunting names—Feuillet, Capus, Donnay, Tinayre, Boylesve,
Bazin, Theuriet—and all the rest of them—must have
known all the sweat and anguish of hard labor, the solici-
tude, the grinding effort, and the desperate patience,
that every artist knows, he became obsessed, haunted
with the idea that the works of all this graceful, strange,
and fortunate company were written without effort,
with the most superb casualness and ease. It was his
strange delusion that all of them were not only of an

equal talent—could do all kinds of writing equally well and with equal ease—but that the reason for this marvellous endowment lay somehow in the fact that they were "French"—that by the fortunate accident of race and birth each one had somehow been constituted an artist who could do all things gracefully and well, and could do nothing wrong. Favored at birth by the great inheritance of their language, blood, and temperament, they grew up as children of a beautiful, strange, and legendary civilization whose very tongue was a guaranty of style, whose very tradition an assurance of form. These men could write nothing badly because it was not within the blood and nature of their race to do so: they must do everything gracefully, easily, and with an impeccable sense of form, because grace and ease and form were innate, with them.

Finally, the most extraordinary fact of this curious obsession was his belief that all these books had been written by their authors not in the stern and lonely solitude of some midnight room, but swiftly, casually, and easily, as one might write a letter at the table of a café.

The obsession was so strong that he could see them writing at such a place—Feuillet, Capus, Donnay, Bazin —all the rest of them, each seated in the afternoon at his own inviolable table in his favorite café, each with a writing pad, a pen and ink before him, a half-emptied bock or glass of wine beside him, an adoring and devoted old waiter hovering anxiously near him—each writing steadily, rapidly, and gracefully the pages of some new and faultless story, some graceful, perfect book, filling up page after page of manuscript in their elegant, fine handwriting, without erasures or deletions, pausing thoughtfully from time to time to stare dreamily away, stroking their lank, disordered hair, their elegant French whiskers with a thin white hand, and so far from being distracted by the gaiety, the noise and clatter of the café crowd around them, deriving a renewed vitality from its sparkling stimulation, and returning to fill up page after page again.

And he could see them meeting every afternoon—that band of Bohemian immortality, that fortunate and favored company of art that could do no wrong—in some café on the Boulevards, or in some quiet, gracious old place hallowed by their patronage, in the Latin Quarter, in Montparnasse, or on the Boul St. Mich or in Montmartre.

He saw the whole scene with a blazing imagery, an exact detail, as if he had himself been present and seen and heard it all. He could hear the spirited light clamor of their conversation—like everything they did, gracious, faultless, full of ease—could see them rise to greet their famous comrades—whoever they might be—Feuillet, Capus, or Donnay, all the rest of them—could see them shake hands with the swift, firm greeting, so graceful, worldly, and so French, and hear them saying:

"Ah, my dear Maurice—how goes it with you? But— I see that I disturb you—pardon, my friend!—I see that you are busy with another of your admirable tales— Ah-h, my old one, not for the world would I disturb the

flow of your so admirable genius. Parbleu! Do I wish
my wretched name to become infamous to all posterity,
to be heard with execration—ah, the devil! Non! The
black forgetfulness of the grave is better! Eh, well, then,
old comrade, till tomorrow—*Then* I hope——"

"Ah, but no, but no, but no, but no, but no! My dear
Octave, you shall remain! These pages here!—Pouf! it
is nothing! I am already done—Attend!" Swiftly he
scrawls a line or two, and then triumphantly: "Voilà!
C'est fini, old cock! A trifle I was finishing for my scoun-
drel of a publisher, who demands it for tomorrow.—
But, tell me, my dear boy—what the devil kept you in
the provinces for so long a time—so long away from this
dear Pa-ree? Ah, how we have missed you: my dear
fellow, Paris really never is the same unless you are here
to give it grace! Tiens! Tiens! Poor Courteline has been
quite inconsolable! Capus has sworn daily he would go
and fetch you back! Tinayre is grouchy as a bear! My
dear fellow, we have all lamented you! De Régnier was
certain you had got another mistress! Boylesve insisted
that she was at least a duchess—Bazin, a milkmaid——"

"And you, my old one?"

"I? My dear fellow—I knew it must be chicken-pox
or measles: I was certain you would not have to stir a
foot out of Pa-ree to find a wench."

"But tell me, Octave, how are all our friends? I am
starved for news, I have read nothing. First of all—
René——?"

"Has published another admirable work—an excellent study of life in the provinces."

"Ah, good! And Duvernois?"

"His latest comedy has been produced and is un succès fou—a charming thing—witty, naughty, quite in his best vein, my dear boy."

"Renard?"

"A comedy, a book of stories, a romance—all excellent, all doing well."

"And Courteline?"

"Une chose incomparable, my boy: a book of dialogues in his drollest vein—the public is convulsed: the police are in a towering rage about *Le Gendarme est san Pitié*——"

"And Abel?"

"A formidable book, my lad—just what you would expect, a powerful tragedy, exact psychology, brilliant —but here he comes, all smiles—ah-h! I thought so! He sees you—My dear Abel, welcome: behold, our prodigal has come home again——"

Yes, it was so that it was done, without anguish, error, or maddening of the soul.

And far, far away from all this certain grace, this ease of form, this assured attaining of expression—there lay America—and all the dumb hunger of its hundred million tongues, its unfound form, its unborn art. Far, far away from this enchanted legend of a city—there lay America and the brutal stupefaction of its million streets, its unquiet heart, its vast incertitude, the huge sprawled welter of its life—its formless and illimitable distances.

And Great God! Great God! but it was farther,

stranger than a dream—he noted its cruelty, savagery, horror, error, loss and waste of life, its brutal criminality, and its hypocritic mask of virtue, its lies, its horrible falseness, and its murderous closure of a telling tongue—and Great God! Great God! with every pulse and fibre in him, with the huge, sick ache of an intolerable homelessness, he was longing with every beat of his anguished heart for just one thing—*return!*

Opulent Fantasies

T O FIND old cities as they were, unruined—the
picture charmed him. The Lost Atlantis. Ville
d'Ys. The old lost towns, seasunken. Great vacant ways, unrusted, echoed under his lonely
feet; he haunted vast arcades, he pierced the atrium,
his shoes rang on the temple flags.

Or to be, he lusciously meditated, left alone with a
group of pretty women in a town whence all the other
people had fled from some terror of plague, earthquake,
volcano, or other menace to which he, quite happily,
was immune. Lolling his tongue delicately, he saw himself loafing sybaritically through first-class confectioners'
and grocers' shops, gorging like an anaconda on im-
ported dainties: exquisite small fish from Russia,
France, and Sardinia; coal-black hams from England;
ripe olives, brandied peaches, and liqueur chocolates.
He would loot old cellars for fat Burgundies, crack the
gold necks of earth-chilled bottles of Pol Roger against
the wall, and slake his noonday thirst at the spouting
bung of a great butt of *Münchener dunkles*. When his
linen was soiled he would outfit himself anew with silk

underwear and the finest shirtings; he would have a new hat every day in the week and new suits whenever he pleased.

He would occupy a new house every day, and sleep in a different bed every night, selecting the most luxurious residence ultimately for permanent occupancy, and bringing together in it the richest treasures of every notable library in the city. Finally when he wanted a woman from the small group that remained and that spent its time in weaving new enticements for him, he would summons her by ringing out the number he had given her on the Court House bell.

He wanted opulent solitude. His dark vision burned on kingdoms under the sea, on windy castle crags, and on the deep elf kingdoms at the earth's core. He groped for the doorless land of faery, that illimitable haunted country that opened somewhere below a leaf or a stone. And no birds sing.

More practically, he saw for himself great mansions in the ground, grottoes buried in the deep heart of a hill, vast chambers of brown earth, sumptuously appointed with his bee-like plunder. Cool hidden cisterns would bring him air; from a peephole in the hillside he could look down on a winding road and see armed men seeking for him, or hear their thwarted gropings overhead. He would pull fat fish from subterranean pools, his great earth cellars would be stocked with old wine, he could loot the world of its treasures, including the handsomest women, and never be caught.

King Solomon's mines. She. Proserpine. Ali Baba.

Orpheus and Eurydice. Naked came I from my mother's womb. Naked shall I return. Let the mothering womb of earth engulf me. Naked, a valiant wisp of man, in vast brown limbs engulfed.

Old Men and Women

S O LONG ago. I have lived so long. I have seen so
much. I could tell you so many things," his uncle
said huskily, with weariness and indifference.
His eye was lustreless and dead, he looked for a
moment tired and old.

All at once, a strange and perplexing vision, which
was to return many times in the years that followed,
came to the boy. It was this: there was a company of
old men and women at dinner, seated together around a
table. All of them were very old, older than his uncle;
the faces of the old men and women were fragile and
delicate like old yellowed china, their faces were frail
and sexless, they had begun to look alike. In their youth
all these people had known one another. The men had
drunk, fought, whored, hated one another, and loved

the women. Some had been devoured by the sterile and corrupt fear and envy that young men know. In secret their lips were twisted, their faces livid, and their hearts bitter; their eyes glittered with a reptilian hatred of another man—they dreaded his success, and they exulted in his failure, laughing with a delirious joy when they heard or read of his hurt, defeat, or humiliation. They had been afraid to speak or confess what was in their hearts, they feared the mockery of their fellows; with one another their words were careful, picked, and disparaging. They gave the lie to passion and belief and they said what they knew was false. And yet along dark roads at night they had shouted out into the howling winds their great goat cries of joy, exultancy and power; they had smelled snow in thick brooding air at night, and they had watched it come, softly spitting at the window glass, numbing the footfalls of the earth with its soft silent fall, filling their hearts with a dark proud ecstasy, touching their entrails with impending prophecy. Each had a thousand dark desires and fantasies; each wanted wealth, power, fame and love; each saw himself as great, good and talented; each feared and hated rivals in business or in love—and in crowds they glared at one another with hard hostile eyes, they bristled up like crested cocks, they watched their women jealously, felt looks and glances through their shoulderblades, and hated men with white spermatic necks, amorous hair, and faces proud and insolent with female conquest.

They had been young and full of pain and combat,

and now all this was dead in them: they smiled mildly, feebly, gently, they spoke in thin voices, and they looked at one another with eyes dead to desire, hostility, and passion.

As for the old women, they sat there on their yellowed and bony haunches. They were all beyond the bitter pain and ecstasy of youth—its frenzy, its hope, its sinew of bright blood and agony: they were beyond the pain and fear of anything save age and death. Here was a faithful wife, a fruitful mother; here was an adulterous and voluptuous woman, the potent mistress of a dozen men, here was her cuckold husband, who had screamed like a tortured animal when he had first found her in bed with another man, and here was the man he found her with; here was another man in whom the knowledge of his wife's infidelity had aroused only a corrupt inverted joy, he exulted in it, he urged her on into new love affairs, he besought her greedily to taunt him with it, he fed upon his pain—and now they were all old and meagre and had the look of yellowed china. They turned their mild sunken faces toward one another with looks in which there was neither hate nor love nor desire nor passion, they laughed thinly, and their memory was all of little things.

They no longer wanted to excel or to be first; they were no longer mad and jealous; they no longer hated rivals; they no longer wanted fame; they no longer cared for work or grew drunk on hope; they no longer turned into the dark and struck their bloody knuckles at the wall; they no longer writhed with shame upon their beds, cursed at the memory of defeat and desolation, or ripped the sheets between convulsive fingers. Could they not speak? Had they forgotten?

Why could not the old men speak? They had known pain, death and madness, yet all their words were stale and rusty. They had known the wilderness, the savage land, the blood of the murdered men ran down into the earth that gave no answer; and they had seen it, they had shed it. Where were the passion, pain and pride, the million living moments of their lives? Was all this lost? Were they all tongueless? It seemed to the boy that there was something sly and evil in their glances as they sat together, as if they hoarded some cunning and malevolent wisdom in their brains, as if the medicine to all our grief and error was in them, but as if through the evil and conspirate communication of their glance, they had resolved to keep it from us. Or were they simply devoured with satiety, with weariness and indifference? Did they refuse to speak because they could not speak, because even memory had gone lifeless in them?

Yes. Words echoed in their throat but they were tongueless. For them the past was dead: they poured into our hands a handful of dry dust and ashes.

The dry bones, the bitter dust? The living wilderness, the silent waste? The barren land?

Have no lips trembled in the wilderness? No eyes sought seaward from the rock's sharp edge for men returning home? Has no pulse beat more hot with love or hate upon the river's edge? Or where the old wheel and the rusted stock lie stogged in desert sand: by the horsehead a woman's skull. No love?

No lonely footfalls in a million streets, no heart that beat its best and bloodiest cry out against the steel and stone, no aching brain, caught in its iron ring, groping among the labyrinthine canyons? Naught in that immense and lonely land but incessant growth and ripeness and pollution, the emptiness of forests and deserts, the unhearted, harsh and metal jangle of a million tongues, crying the belly-cry for bread, or the great cat's snarl for meat and honey? All, then, all? Birth and the twenty thousand days of snarl and jangle—and no love, no love? Was no love crying in the wilderness?

It was not true. The lovers lay below the lilac bush; the laurel leaves were trembling in the wood.

Spring Night in the City

I T WAS now early morning, about half-past three
o'clock, with a sky full of blazing and delicate stars,
an immense and lilac darkness, a night still cool,
and full of chill, but with all the lonely and jubilant
exultancy of spring in it. Far-off, half-heard, immensely
mournful, wild with joy and sorrow, there was a ship
lowing in the darkness, a great boat blowing at the
harbor's mouth.

The street looked dark, tranquil, almost deserted—as
quiet as it could ever be, and at that brief hour when
all its furious noise and movement of the day seemed
stilled for a moment's breathing space, and yet prepar-
ing for another day. The taxis drilled past emptily,
sparely, and at intervals, like projectiles, the feet of
people made a lean and picketing noise upon the pavements, the lights burned green and red and yellow with
a small hard lonely radiance that somehow filled the
heart with strong joy and victory, and belonged to the
wild exultancy of the night, the ships, the springtime,
and of April.

[200]

And again, I looked and saw the deathless sky, the huge starred visage of the night, and heard the boats then on the river. And instantly an enormous sanity and hope of strong exultant joy surged up in me again; and like a man who knows he is mad with thirst, yet sees real rivers at the desert's edge, I knew I should not die and strangle like a mad dog in the tunnel's dark. I knew I should see light once more and know new coasts and come into strange harbors, and see again, as I had once, new lands and morning.

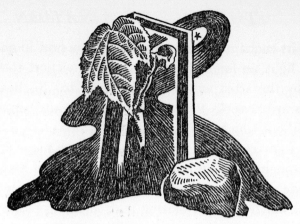

Life's Hungry Man

THE sense and sight and assurance of these things acted like a powerful and gloriously intoxicating liquor on his heart and mind and spirit. He felt an overpowering surge of warm affection, proud and tender gratefulness towards Joel and his sister. It seemed to him that they were the finest people he had ever known—the most generous, the truest, highest, and the loyalest—and the knowledge that they liked his play—were in fact conquered and possessed, brought out of themselves and laid under the play's power and magic—his *own* power and magic—overwhelmed him for a moment with a feeling of the purest, highest, and most glorious happiness that life can yield—the happiness that is at once the most selfish and the most selfless—the happiness of the artist when he sees that his work has been found good, has won for itself a place of honor, glory, and proud esteem in the hearts of men, and has wrought upon their lives the spell of its enchantment. At that instant he saw, in one blaze of light, an image of unutterable conviction, the reason why the artist works and lives and has his being—the reward he seeks—the only reward he really cares about, without which there is nothing. It is to snare the spirits of mankind in nets of magic, to make his life prevail through his creation, to wreak the vision of his life, the rude and painful substance of his own experience, into the congruence of blazing and enchanted images that are themselves the core of life, the essential pattern whence all other things proceed, the kernel of eternity. This is the reason that the artist lives and works and has his being: that from life's clay and his own nature, and from his father's common earth of toil and sweat and violence and error and bitter anguish, he may distil the beauty of an everlasting form, enslave and conquer man by his enchantment, cast his spell across the generations, beat death down upon his knees, kill death utterly, and fix eternity with the grappling-hooks of his own art. His life is soul-hydroptic with a quenchless thirst for glory, and his spirit tortured by the anguish of possession—the intolerable desire to fix eternally in the patterns of an indestructible form a single moment of man's living, a single moment of life's beauty, passion, and unutterable eloquence, that passes, flames and goes, slipping forever through our fingers with time's sanded drop, flowing forever from our desperate grasp even as a river flows and never can be held. This is the artist, then—life's hungry man, the glutton of eternity, beauty's miser, glory's slave—and to do these things, to get the

[203]

Echoes of Forgotten Time

P LAY us a tune on an unbroken spinet, and let
the bells ring, let the bells ring! Play music now:
play us a tune on an unbroken spinet. Do not
make echoes of forgotten time, do not strike music from old broken keys, do not make ghosts with faded
tinklings on the yellowed board; but play us a tune on
an unbroken spinet, play lively music when the instru-
ment was new, let us see Mozart playing in the parlor,
and let us hear the sound of the ladies' voices. But more
than that; waken the turmoil of forgotten streets, let us
hear their sounds again unmuted, and unchanged by
time, throw the light of Wednesday morning on the
Third Crusade, and let us see Athens on an average
day. Let us hear the sound of the voices of the Greeks,
and observe closely if they were all wise and beautiful

at ten o'clock in the morning; let us see if their limbs were all perfect, and their gestures grave and stately, also let us smell their food and observe them eating, and hear, if only once, the sound of a wheel in a street, the texture of just four forgotten moments.

Give us the sounds of Egypt on a certain day; let us hear the voice of King Menkaura and some of the words of the Lady Sennuwy; also the voices of the cotton-farmers. Let us hear the vast and casual sound of life, in these old peoples: their greetings in the street, the voices of the housewives and the merchants. And let us hear the laughter of a woman in the sixteenth century.

The cry of the wolf would always be the same; the sound of the wheel will always be the same; and the hoof of the horse on the roads of every time will be the same. But play us a tune on an unbroken spinet; and let us hear the voices of the knights at dinner. The cry of a man to his dog, and the barking of the dog; the call of the plow-driver to his horse, and the sound of the horse; the noise of the hunt, and the sound of the flowing water, will always be the same.

By the waters of life, by time, by time, play us a tune on an unbroken spinet, and let us hear the actual voices of old fairs; let us move backward through our memories, and through the memory of the race, let us relive the million forgotten moments of our lives, and let us see poor people sitting in their rooms in 1597, and let us see the rich man standing with his back before the fire, in the Middle Ages, and his wife knitting by the table, and let us hear their casual words.

Let us see the men who built the houses of Old Frank-
fort; let us see how they worked, and let us see them
sitting on hewn timbers when they ate their lunches;
let us hear their words, the sound of their voices. Unwind the fabric of lost time out of our entrails, repair
the million little threads of actual circumstance until
the seconds grow gray, bright and dusty with the living
light, and we see the plain unfabled faces of the people;
let us awake, and hear the people in the streets, and see
Tobias Smollett pass our window.

Then, play us a tune on the unbroken spinet, let time
be as the road to London and we a traveller on it; and
let us enter London and find out what year it is there in
the Mile End Road; let it be dark, and let us enter
London in the dark, and hear men's voices, and let us
see if we could understand them; and let us then find
out what year it is, a lodging for the night, and see if
they read mystery on us, or would fly away from us.

But there are times that are stranger yet, there are
times that are stranger than the young knights and the
horses, and the sounds of the eating taverns. The far
time is the time of yesterday: it is the time of early
America, it is the voices of the people on Broadway in
1841, it is the sounds of the streets in Des Moines in
1887, it is the engines of the early trains at Baltimore
in 1853, it is the faces and voices of the early American
people, who are lapped up in the wilderness, who are
hid from us, whose faces are in mystery, whose lives are
more dark and strange than the lives of the Saxon
thanes.

The time that is lovely is the time of the fatness and of the bright colors; it is the elfin time of the calendars, and the sad and mysterious time of the early photographs. It is the time of the early lithographs, it is the time when the world was green and red and yellow. It is the time of the red barn and the windmill, and the house of the seven thousand gables; it is the time of the green lawn and the blue sky and the white excursion-steamer in the river, and the flags, the streamers, the gay brown-and-white buntings, the brass bands and the tumult of all the people who cry out Hurray, hurray!

It is the time of the boy rolling his hoop down the pink path, and of Mama in a bonnet and with a muff, and a stuck-out bottom, and Papa with a derby; it is the time of peace and plenty and the fair stripes of color, and the iron stag. It is the time of the lightning-rod salesman and the summer boarder, it is the time of Farmer Hayseed and of Dusty Rhodes the tramp, it is the time when boys started on the downward path through cigarettes; it is a lovely time. It is the time of the lures and snares of the wicked city and of the Great White Way; it is the time of pitfalls that await the innocent country girl with a whaleboned collar and a small waist; it is the time of Palaces of Sin or the Devil in Society; it is the time of the Tenderloin, of the nests of vice; it is the time of the gilded resorts with mirrors and soft carpets, where the mechanical piano played and you bought champagne, and of the High Class places and the Madam who would not stand for any ungentlemanly behavior, the time of the girls who wore evening dresses and were Perfect Ladies.

It is the time of the opera and theatre parties, and the Horse Show, and of late jolly suppers in the walnut dining-rooms; it is the time of elegant ladies with long gloves on naked arms, and Welsh rarebit in the chafing-dish; it is the time of the Four Hundred, and the great names of the millionaires—the Vanderbilts, the Astors, and the Goulds—it is the time of the powdered flunkies and the twenty-dollar favors; it is the time of Newport, and the canopied red-carpeted sidewalks, and the great mansions on Fifth Avenue, and the splendid gilt and plush marble halls, and the time of the fortune-hunting foreign noblemen (London papers please copy).

It is the time of the effeminate fop, and the lisping ass (Oh, Percy! I'll slap you on your wrist, you rough, rude thing, you!); it is the time of the Damned Dude who wears English clothes and has cuffs on his trousers (Hey! mister! Is it raining in London?), and he never did anything in his life but spend his old man's money, he never did an honest lick of work in his life, he's not worth powder enough to kill him, and if the son-of-a-bitch comes fooling around any sister of mine I'll beat the everlasting tar out of him.

When the songs that they sang were old and sweet, when the songs that they sang were like beauty's from afar, and when people sitting on their porches in the dusk could hear (O sweet and low!) the corner quartette sing, "Sweet Adeline"; when the songs that they sang were "Daisy, Daisy, Give Me Your Answer True."

It is the time of the wharves and the tangled shipping, the horse-cars by the docks, of piled-up casks and kegs of rum and molasses. There are forgotten fume-flaws of bright smoke above Manhattan; where are the lost faces that came towards us over Brooklyn bridge, where are the parted ripples and the proud forgotten ships?

By the waters of life, before we knew that we must die, before we had seen our father's face, before we had sought the print of his foot: by the waters of time (the tide! the tide!), before we had seen the shadows in the haunted woods, before lost moments lived again, before the shades were fleshed. Who are we, that must follow in the footsteps of the king? Who are we, that had no kings to follow? We are the unkinged men. Have we left shadows on forgotten walls? Have we crossed running water and lived for seven timeless years with the enchantress, and shall we find our son who is ourself, and will he know us?

Shall your voices unlock the gates of my brain? Shall I know you, though I have never seen your face? Will you know me, and will you call me "son"? Father, I know that you live, though I have never found you.

Voices of the Books

H E STAYED there long into the night in that
rich room, while the great house sank into sleep
and silence all around him. And at first he
moved there quietly like a man living in an
enchanted dream, almost afraid to draw a breath lest he

dispel the glory and the magic of enchantment, and all the time the voices of the living books around him seemed to speak to him, to say to him: "Now it is night and silence and the sleeptime of the earth, the all-exultant time of youth and loneliness, and of your spirit's proud accession. Now take us, plunder us and take us, for you are alone and living in the world tonight while all the sleepers sleep, immortal knowledge will be yours tonight, the secrets of an everlasting and triumphal wisdom; the huge compacted treasure of the earth speaks to you from these storied shelves, and it is yours, you are the richest man in all the earth if you will take us, only take us, we have waited for you long, dear friend, tonight the world is yours, and will be yours for-ever, if you will only take us, take us, take us."

And like a man drunk with joy, half through the night he plundered the living treasure of those shelves. They were all there—the great chroniclers and recorders, the marvellous and enchanted lies of old Herodotus, and Sir Thomas Malory, and the voyages of Hakluyt and of Purchas, the histories of Mandeville and Hume. There was Burton's marvellous *Anatomy*, his staggering eru-dition never smelling of the dust or of the lamp, his lusty, pungent ever-rushing-onward style, and the anni-hilating irony of Gibbon's latinized sonority, and the savage, burning, somehow magic plainness of Swift's style. There was the dark tremendous music of Sir Thomas Browne, and Hooker's sounding and tremen-dous passion made great by genius and made true by faith, and there was the giant dance, the vast storm-rounding cadence, now demented and now strong as light, of great Carlyle; and beside the haunting cadences of this tremendous piece, there was the pungent world-liness of life-loving men; the keen diaries of John Evelyn, the lusty tang and calculation and sensual rumi-nation of old Pepys, the writing bright as noon, natural as morning, and the plain and middle-magic of the eighteenth century, the flawless grace and faultless clearness of Addison and Steele, and then all the pag-eantry of living character, the pages crowded with the immortal flesh of Sterne, Defoe, and Smollett, the huge comic universe of Fielding, the little one of Austen, and the immortal and extravagant one of Charles Dick-ens, the magnificent proliferation of Sir Walter Scott's tremendous gallery—and Thackeray's sentimental gal-lantry and magic, and all the single magics of Nathaniel Hawthorne, of Meredith, and Melville, of Landor, Pea-cock, Lamb, and of De Quincey, of Hazlitt, and of Poe.

There were as well, the works of all the poets, the Kelmscott Chaucers, the Dove editions, the doe-skin bindings, white and soft and velvet to the touch, the splendid bodies in all their royal pageantry of blue and gold and dense rich green—the Greek anthologies and all the poets of antiquity, and the singing voices of the great Elizabethans—of Wyatt, Surrey, Sidney, and of Spenser, Webster, Ford and Massinger, of Kyd and Greene and Marlowe, of Beaumont, Lyly, Nash and Dekker, of Jonson, Shakespeare, Herrick, Herbert, Donne.

They were all there, from thundering Æschylus to the

sweet small voice of perfect singing Herrick, from grand plain Homer to poignant Catullus, from acid and tart-humored Horace, from the lusty, vulgar and sweet-singing voice of Geoffrey Chaucer, the great bronze ring and clangorous sonority of John Dryden, to the massy gold, the choked-in richness, the haunting fall and faery, of John Keats.

They were all there—each stored there in his little niche upon the living shelves, and at first he looted them, he plundered through their golden leaves as a man who first discovers a buried and inestimable treasure, and at first is dumb with joy at his discovery, and can only plunge his hands in it with drunken joy, scoop handfuls up and pour it over him and let the massy gold leak out again in golden ruin through his spread hands; or as a man who discovers some enchanted spring of ageless youth, of ever-living immortality, and drinks of it, and can never drink enough, and drinks and feels with every drink the huge summation of earth's glory in his own enrichment, the ageless fires of its magic youth.

Then, as the night wore on, another feeling crept across his heart, the living voices of the books spoke to him with another tone. From those great tongues of life and power and soaring immortality there had now departed all the sonorous conviction of their overwhelming, all-triumphant chant. The grand and ringing tongue and joy now spoke the language of a quiet and illimitable despair, confided the legend of an inevitable defeat, an inexorable fatality.

From those high storied shelves of dense rich bindings the great voices of eternity, the tongues of mighty poets dead and gone, now seemed to speak to him out of the living and animate silence of the room. But in that living silence, in the vast and quiet spirit of sleep which filled the great house, amid the grand and overwhelming stillness of that proud power of wealth and the impregnable security of its position, even the voices of those mighty poets dead and gone now seemed somehow lonely, small, lost, and pitiful. Each in his little niche of shelf securely stored—all of the genius, richness, and whole compacted treasure of a poet's life within a foot of space, within the limits of six small dense richly-garnished volumes—all of the great poets of the earth were there, unread, unopened, and forgotten, and were somehow, terribly, the mute small symbols of a rich man's power, of the power of wealth to own everything, to take everything, to triumph over everything—even over the power and genius of the mightiest poet—to keep him there upon his little foot of shelf, unopened and forgotten, but possessed.

Thus, for the first time in his life, even the voices of the mighty poets seemed lost and small and pitifully defeated. Their great voices, which had given to the heart of youth the added fire of their triumphant magic, had borne his spirit high upon the wings of the soaring and invincible belief that no might on earth was equal to the might of poetry, no immortality could equal the immortality of a poet's life and fame, no glory touch his glory, or no strength his strength—now seemed to speak

[215]

to him the mute and small and lonely judgment of defeat:

"Child, child," they said to him, "look at us and reflect: what shall it profit you to feed upon the roots of all-engulfing night, desiring glory? Do not the rats of death and age and dark oblivion feed so forever at the roots of sleep, and can you tell us where a man lies buried now whose substance they have not devoured? Oh, child, forever in the dark old house of life to go alone, to prowl the barren avenues of night, and listen while doors swing and creak in the old house of life, and ponder on the lids of night, and ruminate the vast heart of sleep and silence and the dark, and so consume yourself—desiring what? Poor child, you son of an unlettered race, you nameless atom of the nameless wilderness, how have you let us dupe you with our fictive glories? What power is there on earth, in sea or heaven, what power have you in yourself, you son of your unuttered fathers, to find a tongue for your unuttered brothers, and to make a frame, a shape, a magic and eternal form out of the jungle of the great unuttered wilderness from which you came, of which you are a nameless and unuttered atom? What can you hope to do, poor nameless child and would-be chronicler of the huge unhistoried morass of the dark wilderness of America, when we, who were the children of a hundred gold-recorded centuries and the heirs of all the rich accumulations of tradition, have really done so little— and have come to this? What profit do you hope to gain —what reward could you achieve that would repay you for all the anguish, hunger, and the desperate effort of your life? At its rare infrequent best, out of your blind and famished gropings in the jungle depths, you may pluck out a shining word—achieve a moment's flash of grace and intuition—a half-heard whisper of the vast unuttered language that you seek—perhaps a moment's taste of fame, a brief hour's flash of the imagined glory that you thirst for. For just a moment, you, like other men, will play the lion, will feed upon the older lion's blood, will triumph for a moment through his defeat, will taste joy for a moment through the blood of his despair—and then, like him, you too will be thrown to the mercy of the coming lion, the wilderness will rise again to engulf you, your little hour of glory for which your soul thirsts and your life is panting will be over before it has well begun, and the myriad horde of all your thousand mongrel races will rise with snarl and jeer and curse and lie and mocking to do your life to death, with all the hatred of their mongrel rancor and their own self-loathing, to kill the lion they have crowned for just a day, to hurl you back into a nameless and dishonorable oblivion, drowned down beneath the huge mock and jibe of the old scornmaker's pride. Therefore, short-lived, your life will soon be ended; your youth, but just begun, will shortly be consumed, and all the labor of your anguish and your hunger will be mocked to scorn by the same mongrel fools who praised it, and forgotten by the very knaves who gave it fame. Such is the infrequent good, the flash of brief fame, to which you may aspire, the huge oblivion of failure, misery and dishonor which will follow. But if, by miraculous good chance, you should escape from this—be not devoured and slain and drowned out and forgotten in the brutal swarming shades of jungle time—what greater glory is there that you can achieve? Some such as ours, perhaps—then look at us, and see the state to which we've come. To lie forgotten on the rich shelves of a rich man's library—to be a portion of his idle wealth —the evidence of his arrogant possession—to rise, as all the earth must rise—these dreaming hills and haunted woods, the mighty river and this great moon-haunted hill where stands this house—shout the tributes of a rich man's glory—to bow before him—to lie bought, owned, forgotten and possessed—the greatest poets that ever walked the earth or built, like you, great dreams of glory—to be obsequious tributes to a rich man's fame. Yes, you, even you—poor naked child—may come to this —to reach this state, to be entombed here, bought and idle and among the forgotten huge encumbrance of a rich man's arrogant possession—and to know at last that all the glory, genius, and magic of a poet's life may lie condensed in six rich bindings, forgotten, purchased and unread—and finally defeated by the only thing in life that lasts and will triumph forever—the all-consuming tyranny of wealth that makes a slave of its great poets— that makes us the barren whores of fame, the pimps of wealth—unused and empty on a rich man's shelf."

So did that great treasure of unread, purchased, and forgotten books speak to him in the silent watches of the night, as they stood there, lonely, small and bought, on a rich man's shelf. [218]

Lost and Scattered

O THE wonder, the magic and the loss! His life was like a great wave breaking in the lonely sea; his hungry shoulder found no barriers—he smote his strength at nothing, and was lost and scattered like a wrack of mist. But he believed that this supreme ecstasy which mastered him and made him drunken might some day fuse its enormous light into a single articulation. He was Phaeton with the terrible horses of the sun: he believed that his life might pulse constantly at its longest stroke, achieve an eternal summit.

Visions of Horror and of Delight

IN ALL the dreams and visions that now swarmed
across his sleep, dreams and visions which can only
be described as haunted fatally by the sense of time
—his mind seemed to exercise the same complete
control it ever had shown in all the operations of its
conscious memory. He slept, and knew he slept, and saw
the whole vast structure of the sleeping world about him
as he slept; he dreamed, and knew he dreamed, and like
a sorcerer, drew upward at his will, out of dark deeps
and blue immensities of sleep, the strange, dark fish of
his imagining.

Sometimes they came with elvish flakings of a hoary
light, sometimes they came like magic and the promise
of immortal joy, they came with victory and singing
and a shout of triumph in his blood, and again he felt
the strange and deathless joy of voyages: he was a
passenger upon great ships again, he walked the broad,
scrubbed decks exultantly, and smelled the hot, tarred

roofs of powerful and ugly piers, he smelled the spermy sea-wrack of the harbor once again, the wastes of oil, the sharp, acrid and exultant smoke from busy little tugs, the odor of old, worn plankings, drenched with sunlight, and the thousand strange compacted spices of the laden piers. Again he felt the gold and sapphire loveliness of a Saturday in May, and drank the glory of the earth into his heart, and heard in lucent and lyrical air the heavy shattering "baugh" of the great ship's whistle, as it spoke gloriously, of springtime, new lands and departure. Again he saw ten thousand faces, touched with their strange admixture of sorrow and joy, swarm past the openings of the pier, and again he saw the flashing tides that girdled the city, whitened around the prows of a hundred boats, and gleaming with a million iridescent points of light. Again the great walled cliff, the crowded isle, the fabulous spires and ramparts of the city, as delicate as the hues of light that flashed around them, slid away from him, and one by one, the great ships, with the proud sweep of their breasts of white, their opulent storied superstructure, their music of power and speed, fell into line at noon on Saturday. And now, like bridled horses held in rein, with princely chafe and curvetings, they breach the mighty harbor, nose the narrows, circle slowly to brief pauses at the pilot's boat, and then, like racers set loose from the barriers, they are sent away, their engines tremble to a mighty stroke, the ships are given to the sea, to solitude, and to their proper glory once more.

And again he walked the decks, he walked the decks

alone, and saw the glittering sea-flung city melt within his sight, and watched the sandy edges of the land fade away, and felt the incredible gold and sapphire glory of the day, the sparkle of dancing waters, and smelled salt, sea-borne air again, and saw upon the decks the joyful and exultant faces of the passengers, their looks of wonder, hope, and speculation, as they looked into the faces of strange men and women, now by the miracle of the voyage and chance isled with them in the loneliness of water, upon the glorious prison of a ship. And again he saw the faces of the lovely women, and saw the lights of love and passion in their eyes, and again he felt the plangent and depthless undulance, the unforgettable feeling of the fathomless might of the sea beneath a ship; a wild cry was torn from his throat, and a thousand unutterable feelings of the voyage, of white coasts and sparkling harbors and the creaking, eerie cries of gulls, of the dear, green dwelling of the earth again, and of strange, golden cities, potent wines, delicious foods, of women, love, and amber thighs spread amorously in ripe golden hay, of discovery and new lands, welled up in him like deathless song and certitude.

But just as these visions of delight and joy thronged upward through the deep marine of sleep, so, by the same fiat, the same calm order of an imperial will, the visions of a depthless shame, a faceless abomination of horror, an indefinable and impalpable corruption, returned to haunt his brain with their sentences of inexpiable guilt and ruin: under their evil spell he lay tranced upon his bed in a hypnosis of acquiescent horror, in a willing suspension of all his forces of resistance, like some creature held captive before the hypnotic rhythm of a reptile's head, the dull, envenomed fascination of its eye.

He moved on ceaselessly across a naked and accursed landscape and beneath a naked and accursed sky, an exile in the center of a planetary vacancy that, like his guilt and shame, had neither place among things living nor among things dead, in which there was neither vengeance of lightning, nor mercy of burial, in which there was neither shade nor shelter, curve nor bend, nor hill, nor tree, nor hollow, in which—earth, air, sky, and limitless horizon—there was only one vast naked eye, inscrutable and accusing, from which there was no escape, and which bathed his naked soul in its fathomless depths of shame.

And then the vision faded, and suddenly, with the bridgeless immediacy of a dream, he found himself within the narrow canyon of a street, pacing interminably along on endless pavements where there was neither face nor footfall save his own, nor eye, nor window, nor any door that he might enter.

He thought he was walking through the harsh and endless continuity of one of those brownstone streets of which most of the city was constructed fifty years ago, and of which great broken lengths and fragments still remain. These streets, even if visited by some one in his waking hours, by some stranger in the fulness of health and sanity, and under the living and practical light of noon or, more particularly, by some man stunned with drink, who came there at some desolate and empty hour of night, might have a kind of cataleptic horror, a visionary unreality, as if some great maniac of architecture had conceived and shaped the first, harsh, ugly pattern of brown angularity, and then repeated it, without a change, into an infinity of illimitable repetition, with the mad and measureless insistence of an idiot monotony.

And forever he walked the street, under the brown and fatal light that fell upon him. He walked the street, and looked for a house there that was his own, for a door he knew, that he must enter, for some one who was waiting for him in the house, and for the merciful dark wall and door that would hide and shelter him from the immense and naked eye of shame that peered upon him constantly. Forever he walked the street and searched the bleak, untelling façades for the house he knew and had forgotten, forever he prowled along before the endless and unchanging façades of the street, and he never found it, and at length he became aware of a vast sibilant whispering, of an immense conspiracy of subdued and obscene laughter, and of the mockery of a thousand evil eyes, that peered in silence from these bleak façades, and that he could never find or see; and forever he walked the streets alone, and heard the immense and secret whisperings and laughter, and was bathed in the bottomless depths of a wordless shame, and could never find the house he had lost, the door he had forgotten.

The American Wilderness

N<small>O.</small> T<small>HE</small> C<small>ATAWBAN</small> of today is not like this, nor would he want to be. He is not a colonist, a settler, a transplanted European; during his three centuries there in the wilderness, he has become native to the immense and lonely land that he inhabits, during those three centuries he has taken on the sinew and color of that earth, he has acquired a character, a tradition, and a history of his own: it is an obscure history, unknown to the world and not to be found in the pages of books, but it is a magnificent history, full of heroism, endurance, and the immortal silence of the earth. It lives in his heart, it lives in his brain, it lives in his unrecorded actions; and with this knowledge he is content, nor does he feel the need of ballads or Armadas to trick him into glory.

He does not need to speak, he does not need to affirm

or deny, he does not need to assert his power or his achievement, for his heart is a lonely and secret heart, his spirit is immensely brave and humble, he has lived alone in the wilderness, he has heard the silence of the earth, he knows what he knows, and he has not spoken yet. We see him, silent and unheralded, in the brief glare of recorded event—he is there in the ranks of the American Revolution, and eighty years later he is there, gloriously but silently, in the ranks of the Civil War. But his real history is much longer and much more extraordinary than could be indicated by these flares of war: it is a history that runs back three centuries into primitive America, a strange and unfathomable history that is touched by something dark and supernatural, and that goes back through poverty and hardship, through solitude and loneliness and death and unspeakable courage, into the wilderness. For it is the wilderness that is the mother of that nation; it was in the wilderness that the strange and lonely people who have not yet spoken, but who inhabit that immense and terrible land from East to West, first knew themselves; it was in the living wilderness that they faced one another at ten paces and shot one another down; and it is in the wilderness that they still live.

The real history of Old Catawba is not essentially a history of wars or rebellions; it is not a history of politics or corrupt officials; it is not a history of democracy or plutocracy or any form of government; it is not a history of business men, puritans, knaves, fools, saints, or heroes; it is not a history of culture or barbarism.

The real history of Old Catawba is a history of solitude, of the wilderness, and of the eternal earth; it is the history of millions of men living and dying alone in the wilderness; it is the history of the billion unrecorded and forgotten acts and moments of their lives; it is a history of the sun and the moon and the earth, of the sea that feathers eternally against the desolate coasts, and of great trees that smash down in lone solitudes of the wilderness.

The history of Old Catawba is the history of millions of men living alone in the wilderness, it is the history of millions of men who have lived their brief lives in silence upon the everlasting earth, who have listened to the earth and known her million tongues, whose lives were given to the earth, whose bones and flesh are recompacted with the earth, the immense and terrible earth that makes no answer.

O Flower of Love

. . . of wandering forever and the earth again . . . of seed-time, bloom, and the mellow-dropping harvest. And of the big flowers, the rich flowers, the strange unknown flowers.

Where shall the weary rest? When shall the lonely of heart come home? What doors are open for the wanderer? And which of us shall find his father, know his face, and in what place, and in what time, and in what land? Where? Where the weary of heart can abide forever, where the weary of wandering can find peace, where the tumult, the fever, and the fret shall be forever stilled.

Who owns the earth? Did we want the earth that we should wander on it? Did we need the earth that we were never still upon it? Whoever needs the earth shall have the earth: he shall be still upon it, he shall rest within a little place, he shall dwell in one small room forever.

Did he feel the need of a thousand tongues that he sought thus through the moil and horror of a thousand furious streets? He shall need a tongue no longer, he shall need no tongue for silence and the earth: he shall speak no word through the rooted lips, the snake's cold eye will peer for him through sockets of the brain, there will be no cry out of the heart where wells the vine.

The tarantula is crawling through the rotted oak, the adder lisps against the breast, cups fall: but the earth will endure forever. The flower of love is living in the wilderness, and the elmroot threads the bones of buried lovers.

The dead tongue withers and the dead heart rots, blind mouths crawl tunnels through the buried flesh, but the earth will endure forever; hair grows like April on the buried breast and from the sockets of the brain the death flowers grow and will not perish.

O flower of love whose strong lips drink us downward into death, in all things far and fleeting, enchantress of our twenty thousand days, the brain will madden and the heart be twisted, broken by her kiss, but glory, glory, glory, she remains: Immortal love, alone and aching in the wilderness, we cried to you: You were not absent from our loneliness.

Space and Movement

WHEN he got to the South station he had five minutes left to buy his ticket and get on his train. In spite of the lashing storm and the lateness of the hour, that magnificent station, which at that time—before the later "improvements" had reduced it to a glittering sterility of tile and marble—was one of the most thrilling and beautiful places in the world, was still busy with the tides of people that hurry forever through the great stations of America, and that no violence of storm can check.

The vast dingy sweep of the cement concourse outside the train-gates was pungent, as it had always been, with the acrid and powerfully exciting smell of engine smoke, and beyond the gates, upon a dozen tracks, great engines, passive and alert as cats, purred and panted softly, with the couched menace of their tremendous stroke. The engine smoke rose up straight in billowing plumes to widen under vaulting arches, to spread foggily throughout the enormous spaces of the grimy sheds. And beside the locomotives, he could see the burly denimed figures of the engineers, holding flaming torches and an oil-can in their hands as they peered and probed through the shining flanges of terrific pistoned wheels much taller than their heads. And forever, over the enormous cement concourse and down the quays beneath the powerful groomed attentiveness of waiting trains the tides of travellers kept passing, passing, in their everlasting change and weft, of voyage and return —of speed and space and movement, morning, cities, and new lands.

And caught up in the vaulting arches of those immense and grimy sheds he heard again the murmurous sound of time—that sound remote and everlasting, distilled out of all the movement, frenzy, and unceasing fury of our unresting lives, and yet itself detached, as calm and imperturbable as the still sad music of humanity, and which, made up out of our million passing lives, is in itself as fixed and everlasting as eternity.

They came, they paused and wove and passed and thrust and vanished in their everlasting tides, they streamed in and out of the portals of that enormous station in unceasing swarm; great trains steamed in to empty them, and others steamed out loaded with their nameless motes of lives, and all was as it had always

been, moving, changing, swarming on forever like a
river, and as fixed, unutterable in unceasing movement
and in changeless change as the great river is, and time
itself.

And within ten minutes he himself, another grain of
dust borne onward on this ceaseless tide, another nameless atom in this everlasting throng, another wanderer
in America, as all his fathers were before him, was
being hurled into the South again in the huge projectile of a train. The train swept swiftly down the gleaming rails, paused briefly at the Back-Bay station, then
was on its way again, moving smoothly, powerfully,
almost noiselessly now, through the outer stretches of
the small dense web of Boston. The town swept smoothly
past: old blanks of wall, and old worn brick, and sudden
spokes of streets, deserted, lashed with rain, set at the
curbs with glittering beetles of its wet machinery and
empetalled with its wet and sudden blooms of life. The
flushed spoke-wires crossed his vision, lost the moment
that he saw them, his forever, gone, like all things else,
and never to be captured, seen a million times, yet never
known before—as haunting, fading, deathless as a
dream, as brief as is the bitter briefness of man's days,
as lost and lonely as his life upon the mighty breast of
earth, and of America.

Then the great train, gathering now in speed, and
mounting smoothly to the summit of its tremendous
stroke, was running swiftly through the outskirts of the
city, through suburbs and brief blurs of light and then
through little towns and on into the darkness, the wild

and secret loneliness of earth. And he was going home again into the South and to a life that had grown strange as dreams, and to his father who was dying and who had become a ghost and shadow of his father to him, and to the bitter reality of grief and death. And—how, why, for what reason he could not say—all he felt was the tongueless swelling of wild joy. It was the wild and secret joy that has no tongue, the impossible hope that has no explanation, the savage, silent, and sweet exultancy of night, the wild and lonely visage of the earth, the imperturbable stroke and calmness of the everlasting earth, from which we have been derived, wherein again we shall be compacted, on which all of us have lived alone as strangers, and across which, in the loneliness of night, we have been hurled onward in the projectile flight of mighty trains—America.

Then the great train was given to the night and darkness, the great train hurtled through the night across the lonely, wild, and secret earth, bearing on to all their thousand destinations its freight of unknown lives —some to morning, cities, new lands, and the joy of voyages, and some to known faces, voices, and the hills of home—but which to certain fortune, peace, security, and love, no man could say.

Names of the Nation

A<small>T MORNING</small>, in a foreign land, whether upon
the mournful plains of Hungary, or in some
quiet square of Georgian houses, embedded
in the immensity of sleeping London, he
awakes, and thinks of home; or in some small provincial
town of France, he starts up from his sleep at night, he

starts up in the living, brooding stillness of the night, for suddenly he thinks that he has heard there the sounds of America and the wilderness, the things that are in his blood, his heart, his brain, in every atom of his flesh and tissue, the things for which he draws his breath in labor, the things that madden him with an intolerable and nameless pain.

And what are they? They are the whistle-wail of one of the great American engines as it thunders through the continent at night, the sound of the voices of the city streets—those hard, loud, slangy voices, full of violence, humor, and recklessness, now stronger and more remote than the sounds of Asia—the sounds that come up from the harbor of Manhattan in the night— that magnificent and thrilling music of escape, mystery, and joy, with the mighty orchestration of the transatlantics, the hoarse little tugs, the ferryboats and lighters, those sounds that well up from the gulf and dark immensity of night and that pierce the entrails of the listener.

For this will always be one of the immortal and living things about the land, this will be an eternal and unchanging fact about that city whose only permanence is change: there will always be the great rivers flowing around it in the darkness, the rivers that have bounded so many nameless lives, those rivers which have moated in so many changes, which have girdled the wilderness and so much hard, brilliant, and sensational living, so much pain, beauty, ugliness, so much lust, murder, corruption, love, and wild exultancy.

They'll build great engines yet, and grander towers, but always the rivers run, in the day, in the night, in the dark, draining immensely their imperial tides out of the wilderness, washing and flowing by the coasts of the fabulous city, by all the little ticking sounds of time, by all the million lives and deaths of the city. Always the rivers run, and always there will be great ships upon the tide, always great horns are baying at the harbor's mouth, and in the night a thousand men have died while the river, always the river, the dark eternal river, full of strange secret time, washing the city's stains away, thickened and darkened by its dumpings, is flowing by us, by us to the sea.

He awakes at morning in a foreign land, and he thinks of home. He cannot rest, his heart is wild with pain and loneliness, he sleeps, but then he knows he sleeps, he hears the dark and secret spell of time about him; in ancient towns, thick tumbling chimes of the cathedral bells are thronging through the dark, but through the passages of his diseased and unforgetful sleep the sounds and memory of America make way: now it is almost dawn, a horse has turned into a street and in America, there is the sound of wheels, the lonely clop-clop of the hooves upon deserted pavements, silence, then the banging clatter of a can.

He awakes at morning in a foreign land, he draws his breath in labor in the wool-soft air of Europe: the wool-gray air is all about him like a living substance; it is in his heart, his stomach, and his entrails; it is in the slow and vital movements of the people; it soaks down from the sodden skies into the earth, into the heavy buildings, into the limbs and hearts and brains of living men. It soaks into the spirit of the wanderer; his heart is dull with the gray weariness of despair, it aches with hunger for the wilderness, the howling of great winds, the bite and sparkle of the clear, cold air, the buzz, the tumult and the wild exultancy. The wet, woolen air is all about him, and there is no hope. It was there before William the Conqueror; it was there before Clovis and Charles "the Hammer"; it was there before Attila; it was there before Hengist and Horsa; it was there before Vercingetorix and Julius Agricola.

It was there now; it will always be there. They had it in Merry England and they had it in Gay Paree; and they were seldom merry, and they were rarely gay. The wet, woolen air is over Munich; it is over Paris; it is over Rouen and Madame Bovary; it soaks into England; it gets into boiled mutton and the Brussels sprouts; it gets into Hammersmith on Sunday; it broods over Bloomsbury and the private hotels and the British Museum; it soaks into the land of Europe and keeps the grass green. It has always been there; it will always be there. His eyes are mad and dull; he cannot sleep without the hauntings of phantasmal memory behind the eyes; his brain is overstretched and weary, it gropes ceaselessly around the prison of the skull, it will not cease.

The years are walking in his brain, his father's voice is sounding in his ears, and in the pulses of his blood the tom-tom's beat. His living dust is stored with memory: two hundred million men are walking in his bones; he hears the howling of the wind around forgotten eaves; he cannot sleep. He walks in midnight corridors; he sees the wilderness, the moon-drenched forests; he comes to clearings in the moonlit stubble, he is lost, he has never been here, yet he is at home. His sleep is haunted with the dreams of time; wires throb above him in the whiteness, they make a humming in the noonday heat.

The rails are laid across eight hundred miles of golden wheat, the rails are wound through mountains, they curve through clay-yellow cuts, they enter tunnels, they are built up across the marshes, they hug the cliff and follow by the river's bank, they cross the plains with dust and thunder, and they leap through flatness and the dull scrub-pine to meet the sea.

Then he awakes at morning in a foreign land, and thinks of home.

For we have awaked at morning in a foreign land and heard the bitter curse of their indictment, and we know what we know, and it will always be the same.

"One time!" their voices cried, leaning upon a bar the bitter weight of all their discontent. "One time! I've been back one time—just once in seven years," they said, "and Jesus that was plenty! One time was enough! To hell with that damned country! What have they got now but a lot of cheap spaghetti joints and skyscrapers?" they said. "If you want a drink, you sneak down three back-alleyways, get the once-over from a couple of exprize fighters, and then plank down a dollar for a shot of varnish that would rot the guts out of a goat! . . . And the women!"—the voices rose here with infuriated scorn —"What a nice lot of cold-blooded gold-digging bastards *they've* turned out to be! . . . I spent thirty dollars taking one of 'em to a show, and to a night-club afterward! When bedtime came do you think I got anything out of it? . . . 'You may kiss my little hand,' she says. . . . You may kiss my little—that's what you may do," the voices snarled with righteous bitterness. "When I asked her if she was goin' to come through she started to yell for the cops! . . . A woman who tried to pull one like that over here would get sent to Siberia! . . . A nice country, I don't think! . . . Now, get this! *Me,* I'm a Frenchman, see!" the voice said with a convincing earnestness. "These guys know how to *live,* see! This is my country where I belong, see! . . . Johnny, luh même chose pour mwah et m'seer! . . . Fill 'em up again, kid.

"Carpen-*teer!*" the voices then rose jeeringly, in true accents of French pugnacity. "Sure, I'm a Frenchman— but Carpen-*teer!* Where do yuh get that stuff? Christ, Dempsey could 'a' took that frog the best day that he ever saw! . . . An accident!" the voices yelled. "Whattya mean—an accident? Didn't I see the whole thing with my own eyes? Wasn't I back there then? . . . Wasn't I talkin' t' Jack himself an hour after the fight was over? . . . An accident! Jesus! The only accident was that he let him last four rounds. 'I could have taken him in the first if I wanted to,' Jack says to me. . . .

Sure, I'm a Frenchman!" the voice said with belligerent loyalty. "But Carpen-*teer!* Jesus! Where do you get that stuff?"

And, brother, I have heard the voices you will never hear, discussing the graces of a life more cultured than any you will ever know—and I know and I know, and yet it is still the same.

Bitterly, bitterly Boston one time more! the flying leaf, the broken cloud—"I think," said they, "that we will live here now. I think," they said, "that we are running down to Spain next week so Francis can do a little writing. . . . And really," their gay yet cultivated tones continued, "it's wonderful what you can do here if you only have a little money. . . . *Yes,* my dear!" their refined accents continued in a tone of gay conviction. "It's really quite incredible, you know. . . . I happen to know of a real honest-to-goodness château near Blois that can be had for something less than $7000! . . . It's all rather incredible, you know," those light, half-English tones went on, "when you consider what it takes to live in Brookline! . . . Francis has always felt that he would like to do a little writing, and I feel somehow the atmosphere is better here for all that sort of thing—it really is, you know. Don't you think so?" said those gay and cultivated tones of Boston which you, my brother, never yet have heard. "And after all," those cultivated tones went on in accents of a droll sincerity, "you see all the people here you really *care* to see, I *mean,* you know! They all come to Paris at one time or another—I *mean,* the trouble really is in getting a little

time alone for yourself. . . . Or do you find it so?"
the voices suavely, lightly, asked. . . . "Oh, look! look
at that—there!" they cried with jubilant elation, "I mean
that boy and his girl there, walking along with their
arms around each other! . . . Don't you just a-do-o-re
it? . . . Isn't it too *ma-a-rvelous?*" those refined and
silvery tones went on, with patriotic tenderness. "I
mean, there's something so perfectly sweet and un-self-
conscious about it all!" the voices said with all the cultivated earnestness of Boston! "Now *where?*—where?—
would you see anything like that at home?" the voices
said triumphantly.

(Seldom in Brookline, lady. Oh, rarely, seldom, almost never in the town of Brookline, lady. But on the
Esplanade—did you ever go out walking on the Esplanade at night-time, in the hot and sultry month of
August, lady? They are not Frenchmen, lady: they are
all Jews and Irish and Italians, lady, but the noise of
their kissing is like the noise the wind makes through a
leafy grove—it is like the great hooves of a hundred
thousand cavalry being pulled out of the marshy places
of the earth, dear lady.)

". . . I *mean*—these people really understand that
sort of thing so much better than we do. . . . They're
so much *simpler* about it. . . . I mean, so much more
graceful with that kind of thing. . . . Il faut un peu
de sentiment, n'est-ce pas? . . . Or do you think so?"
said those light, those gay, those silvery, and half-Eng-
lish tones of cultivated Boston, which you, my brother,
never yet have heard.

[241]

(I got you, lady. That was French. I know. . . . But if I felt your leg, if I began by fondling gracefully your leg, if in a somewhat graceful Gallic way I felt your leg, and said, "Chérie! Petite chérie!"—would you remember, lady, this is Paris?)

Oh, bitterly, bitterly, Boston one time more: their silvery voices speak an accent you will never know, and of their loins is marble made, but, brother, there are corn-haired girls named Neilsen out in Minnesota, and the blonde thighs of the Lundquist girl could break a bullock's back.

Oh, bitterly, bitterly, Boston one time more: the French have little ways about them that we do not have, but brother, they're still selling cradles down in Georgia, and in New Orleans their eyes are dark, their white teeth bite you to the bone.

Oh, bitterly, bitterly, Boston, one time more, and of their flesh is codfish made. Big Brother's still waiting for you with his huge, red fist, behind the barn up in the State of Maine, and they're still having shotgun marriages at home.

Oh, brother, there are voices you will never hear— ancestral voices prophesying war, my brother, and rare and radiant voices that you know not of, as they have read us into doom. The genteel voices of Oxenford broke once like chimes of weary, unenthusiastic bells across my brain, speaking to me compassionately its judgment on our corrupted lives, gently dealing with the universe, my brother, gently and without labor—

gently, brother, gently, it dealt with all of us, with easy condescension and amused disdain:

"I'm afraid, old boy," the genteel voice of Oxenford remarked, "you're up against it over thöh. . . . I really am. . . . Thöh's no place thö faw the individual any longah,"—the genteel voice went on, un-individual brother. "Obviously," that tolerant voice instructed me, "obviously, thöh can be no cultuah in a country so completely lackin' in tradition as is yoähs. . . . It's all so objective—if you see what I main—thöh's no place left faw the innah life," it said, O outward brother! ". . . We Europeans have often obsöhved (it's *very* curious, you know) that the *Ameri*can is incapable of any real feelin'—it seems quite impawsible faw him to distinguish between true emotion an' sentimentality— an' he invayably chooses the lattah! . . . *Curious, isn't it?*—or do you think so, brother? Of co'se, thöh is yoäh beastly dreadful sex-prawblem. . . . Yoäh women! . . . Oh, deah, deah! . . . Perhaps we'd bettah say no moah . . . but, thöh you *ah!*"—right in the eye, my brother. "Yoäh country is a matriahky, my deah fellah . . . it really is, you know," . . . if you can follow us, dear brother. "The women have the men in a state of complete subjection . . . the male is rapidly becomin' moah sexless an' emasculated"—that genteel voice of doom went on—"No!—Decidedly you have quite a prawblem befoah you. . . . Obviously thöh can be no cultuah while such a condition puhsists. . . . *That* is why when my friends say to me, 'You ought to see *America,* . . . you really ought, you know,' . . . I say, 'No, thanks. . . . If you don't mind, I'd rathah not. . . . I think I'll stay at home . . . I'm sorry,' " the compassionate tones of Oxenford went on, "but that's the way I feel—it really is, you know. . . . Of co'se, I know you couldn't undahstand my feelin'—faw aftah all, you ah a Yank—but thöh you ah! Sorry!" it said regretfully, as it spoke its courteous but inexorable judgments of eternal exile, brother, and removed forever the possibility of your ever hearing it. "But that's the way I feel! I hope you don't mind," the voice said gently, with compassion.

No, sir, I don't mind. We don't mind, he, she, it, or they don't mind. Nobody minds, sir, nobody minds. Because, just as you say, sir, oceans are between us, seas have sundered us, there is a magic in you that we cannot fathom—a light, a flame, a glory—an impalpable, indefinable, incomprehensible, undeniable something-or-other, something which I can never understand or measure because—just as you say, sir—with such compassionate regret, I am—I am—a Yank.

'Tis true, my brother, we are Yanks. Oh, 'tis true, 'tis true! I am a Yank! Yet, wherefore Yank, good brother? Hath not a Yank ears? Hath not a Yank lies, truths, bowels of mercy, fears, joys, and lusts? Is he not warmed by the same sun, washed by the same ocean, rotted by the same decay, and eaten by the same worms as a German is? If you kill him, does he not die? If you sweat him, does he not stink? If you lie with his wife or his mistress, does she not whore, lie, fornicate and betray, even as a Frenchman's does? If you strip him, is he not

naked as a Swede? Is his hide less white than Baude-
laire's? Is his breath more foul than the King of Spain's?
Is his belly bigger, his neck fatter, his face more hog-
gish, and his eye more shiny than a Munich brewer's?
Will he not cheat, rape, thieve, whore, curse, hate, and
murder like any European? Aye—Yank! But wherefore,
wherefore Yank—good brother?

Brother, have we come then from a fated stock?
Augured from birth, announced by two dark angels,
named in our mother's womb? And for what? For what?
Father-less, to grope our feelers on the sea's dark bed,
among the polyped squirms, the blind sucks and crawls
and sea-valves of the brain, loaded with memory that
will not die? To cry our love out in the wilderness, to
wake always in the night, smiting the pillow in some
foreign land, thinking forever of the myriad sights and
sounds of home?

"While Paris Sleeps!"—By God, while Paris sleeps, to
wake and walk and not to sleep; to wake and walk and
sleep and wake, and sleep again, seeing dawn come at
the window-square that cast its wedge before our glazed,
half-sleeping eyes, seeing soft, hated foreign light, and
breathing soft, dull languid air that could not bite and
tingle up the blood, seeing legend and lie and fable
wither in our sight as we saw what we saw, knew what
we knew.

Sons of the lost and lonely fathers, sons of the wan-
derers, children of hardy loins, the savage earth, the
pioneers, what had we to do with all their bells and
churches? Could we feed our hunger on portraits of the

Spanish king? Brother, for what? For what? To kill the giant of loneliness and fear, to slay the hunger that would not rest, that would not give us rest.

Of wandering forever, and the earth again. Brother, for what? For what? For what? For the wilderness, the immense and lonely land. For the unendurable hunger, the unbearable ache, the incurable loneliness. For the exultancy whose only answer is the wild goat-cry. For a million memories, ten thousand sights and sounds and shapes and smells and names of things that only we can know.

For what? For what? Not for a nation. Not for a people, not for an empire, not for a thing we love or hate.

For what? For a cry, a space, an ecstasy. For a savage and nameless hunger. For a living and intolerable memory that may not for a second be forgotten, since it includes all the moments of our lives, includes all we do and are. For a living memory; for ten thousand memories; for a million sights and sounds and moments; for something like nothing else on earth; for something which possesses us.

For something under our feet, and around us and over us; something that is in us and part of us, and proceeds from us, that beats in all the pulses of our blood.

Brother, for what?

First for the thunder of imperial names, the names of men and battles, the names of places and great rivers, the mighty names of the States. The name of The Wilderness; and the names of Antietam, Chancellorsville, Shiloh, Bull Run, Fredericksburg, Cold Harbor, the Wheat Fields, Ball's Bluff, and the Devil's Den; the names of Cowpens, Brandywine, and Saratoga; of Death Valley, Chickamauga, and the Cumberland Gap. The names of the Nantahalahs, the Bad Lands, the Painted Desert, the Yosemite, and the Little Big Horn; the names of Yancey and Cabarrus counties; and the terrible name of Hatteras.

Then, for the continental thunder of the States: the names of Montana, Texas, Arizona, Colorado, Michigan, Maryland, Virginia, and the two Dakotas; the names of Oregon and Indiana, of Kansas and the rich Ohio; the powerful name of Pennsylvania, and the name of Old Kentucky; the undulance of Alabama; the names of Florida and North Carolina.

In the red-oak thickets, at the break of day, long hunters lay for bear—the rattle of arrows in laurel leaves, the war-cries round the painted buttes, and the majestical names of the Indian Nations: the Pawnees, the Algonquins, the Iroquois, the Comanches, the Blackfeet, the Seminoles, the Cherokees, the Sioux, the Hurons, the Mohawks, the Navajos, the Utes, the Omahas, the Onondagas, the Chippewas, the Crees, the Chickasaws, the Arapahoes, the Catawbas, the Dakotas, the Apaches, the Croatans, and the Tuscaroras; the names of Powhatan and Sitting Bull; and the name of the Great Chief, Rain-In-The-Face.

Of wandering forever, and the earth again: in red-oak thickets, at the break of day, long hunters lay for bear. The arrows rattle in the laurel leaves, and the elmroots thread the bones of buried lovers. There have been war-cries on the Western trails, and on the plains the gunstock rusts upon a handful of bleached bones. The barren earth? Was no love living in the wilderness?

The rails go westward in the dark. Brother, have you seen starlight on the rails? Have you heard the thunder of the fast express?

Of wandering forever, and the earth again—the names of the mighty rails that bind the nation, the wheeled thunder of the names that net the continent: the Pennsylvania, the Union Pacific, the Santa Fé, the Baltimore and Ohio, the Chicago and Northwestern, the Southern, the Louisiana and Northern, the Seaboard Air Line, the Chicago, Milwaukee and Saint Paul, the Lackawanna, the New York, New Haven and Hartford, the Florida East Coast, the Rock Island, and the Denver and Rio Grande.

Brother, the names of the engines, the engineers, and the sleeping-cars: the great engines of the Pacific type, the articulated Mallets with three sets of eight-yoked driving wheels, the 400-ton thunderbolts with J. T. Cline, T. J. McRae, and the demon hawk-eyes of H. D. Campbell on the rails.

The names of the great tramps who range the nation on the fastest trains: the names of the great tramps Oklahoma Red, Fargo Pete, Dixie Joe, Iron Mike, The Frisco Kid, Nigger Dick, Red Chi, Ike the Kike, and The Jersey Dutchman.

By the waters of life, by time, by time, Lord Tennyson stood among the rocks, and stared. He had long hair, his eyes were deep and sombre, and he wore a cape; he was a poet, and there was magic and mystery in his touch, for he had heard the horns of Elf-land faintly blowing. And by the waters of life, by time, by time, Lord Tennyson stood among the cold, gray rocks, and commanded the sea to break—break—break! And the sea broke, by the waters of life, by time, by time, as Lord Tennyson commanded it to do, and his heart was sad and lonely as he watched the stately ships (of the Hamburg-American Packet Company, fares forty-five dollars and up, first-class) go on to their haven under the hill, and Lord Tennyson would that his heart could utter the thoughts that arose in him.

By the waters of life, by time, by time: the names of the mighty rivers, the alluvial gluts, the drains of the continent, the throats that drink America (Sweet Thames, flow gently till I end my song). The names of the men who pass, and the myriad names of the earth that abides forever: the names of the men who are doomed to wander, and the name of that immense and lonely land on which they wander, to which they return, in which they will be buried—America! The immortal earth which waits forever, the trains that thunder on the continent, the men who wander, and the women who cry out, "Return!"

Finally, the names of the great rivers that are flowing in the darkness (Sweet Thames, flow gently till I end my song).

By the waters of life, by time, by time: the names of
the great mouths, the mighty maws, the vast, wet, coil-
ing, never-glutted and unending snakes that drink the
continent. Where, sons of men, and in what other land,
will you find others like them, and where can you match
the mighty music of their names?—The Monongahela,
the Colorado, the Rio Grande, the Columbia, the Tennessee, the Hudson (Sweet Thames!); the Kennebec,
the Rappahannock, the Delaware, the Penobscot, the
Wabash, the Chesapeake, the Swannanoa, the Indian
River, the Niagara (Sweet Afton!); the Saint Law-
rence, the Susquehanna, the Tombigbee, the Nanta-
hala, the French Broad, the Chattahoochee, the Arizona, and the Potomac (Father Tiber!)—these are a
few of their princely names, these are a few of their
great, proud, glittering names, fit for the immense and
lonely land that they inhabit.

Oh, Tiber! Father Tiber! You'd only be a suckling in
that mighty land! And as for you, sweet Thames, flow
gently till I end my song: flow gently, gentle Thames,
be well-behaved, sweet Thames, speak softly and po-
litely, little Thames, flow gently till I end my song.

By the waters of life, by time, by time, and of the
yellow cat that smites the nation, of the belly of the
snake that coils across the land—of the terrible names
of the rivers in flood, the rivers that foam and welter
in the dark, that smash the levees, that flood the lowlands for two thousand miles, that carry the bones of the
cities seaward on their tides: of the awful names of the
Tennessee, the Arkansas, the Missouri, the Mississippi,

and even the little mountain rivers, brothers, in the season of the floods.

Delicately they dive for Greeks before the railway station: the canoe glides gently through the portals of the waiting room (for whites). Full fathom five the carcass of old man Lype is lying (of his bones is coral made) and delicately they dive for lunch-room Greeks before the railway station.

Brother, what fish are these? The floatage of sunken rooms, the sodden bridal-veils of poverty, the slime of ruined parlor plush, drowned faces in the family album; and the blur of long-drowned eyes, blurred features, whited, bloated flesh.

Delicately they dive for Greeks before the railway station. The stern, good, half-drowned faces of the brothers Trade and Mark survey the tides. Cardui! Miss Lillian Leitzell twists upon one arm above the flood; the clown, half-sunken to his waist, swims upward out of swirling yellow; the tiger bares his teeth above the surges of a river he will never drink. The ragged tatters of the circus posters are plastered on soaked boards. And delicately they dive for Greeks before the railway station.

Have we not seen them, brother?

For what are we, my brother? We are a phantom flare of grieved desire, the ghostling and phosphoric flicker of immortal time, a brevity of days haunted by the eternity of the earth. We are an unspeakable utterance, an insatiable hunger, an unquenchable thirst; a lust that bursts our sinews, explodes our brains, sickens and rots our guts, and rips our hearts asunder. We are a twist of passion, a moment's flame of love and ecstasy, a sinew of bright blood and agony, a lost cry, a music of pain and joy, a haunting of brief, sharp hours, an almost captured beauty, a demon's whisper of unbodied memory. We are the dupes of time.

For, brother, what are we?

We are the sons of our father, whose face we have never seen, we are the sons of our father, whose voice we have never heard, we are the sons of our father, to whom we have cried for strength and comfort in our agony, we are the sons of our father, whose life like ours was lived in solitude and in the wilderness, we are the sons of our father, to whom only can we speak out the strange, dark burden of our heart and spirit, we are the sons of our father, and we shall follow the print of his foot forever.

Spring Plowing

A LIGHT wind of April fanned over the hill. There was a smell of burning leaves and rubble around the school. In the field on the hill flank behind the house a plowman drove his big horse with loose clanking traces around a lessening square of dry fallow earth. Gee, woa. His strong feet followed after. The big share bit cleanly down, cleaving a deep spermy furrow of moist young earth along its track.

John Dorsey Leonard stared fascinated out the window at the annual rejuvenation of the earth. Before his eyes the emergent nymph was scaling her hard cracked hag's pelt. The golden age returned.

Down the road a straggling queue of boys were all gone into the world of light. Wet with honest sweat, the plowman paused at the turn, and wiped the blue shirting of his forearm across his beaded forehead. Meanwhile, his intelligent animal, taking advantage of the interval, lifted with slow majesty a proud flowing tail, and added his mite to the fertility of the soil with three moist oaty droppings. Watching, John Dorsey grunted approvingly. They also serve who only stand and wait.

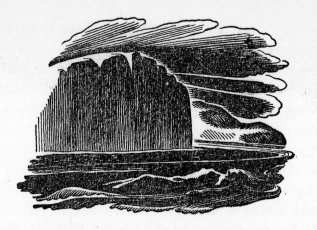

Waters of Darkness

THE river is a tide of moving waters: by night
it floods the pockets of the earth. By night it
drinks strange time, dark time. By night the
river drinks proud potent tides of strange dark
time. By night the river drains the tides, proud potent
tides of time's dark waters that, with champ and lift of
teeth, with lapse and reluctation of their breath, fill
with a kissing glut the pockets of the earth. Sired by the
horses of the sea, maned with the dark, they come.

They come! Ships call! The hooves of night, the
horses of the sea, come on below their manes of darkness. And forever the river runs. Deep as the tides of
time and memory, deep as the tides of sleep, the river
runs.

And there are ships there! Have we not heard the
ships there? (Have we not heard the great ships going

down the river? Have we not heard the great ships
putting out to sea?)

Great whistles blow there. Have we not heard the
whistles blow there? Have we not heard the whistles
blowing on the river? (A harness of bright ships is on
the water. A thunder of faint hooves is on the land.)

And there is time there. (Have we not heard strange
time, dark time, strange tragic time there? Have we
not heard dark time, strange time, the dark, the moving
tide of time as it flows down the river?)

And in the night time, in the dark there, in all the
sleeping silence of the earth, have we not heard the
river, the rich immortal river, full of its strange dark
time?

Full with the pulse of time it flows there, full with
the pulse of all men living, sleeping, dying, waking, it
will flow there, full with the billion dark and secret
moments of our lives it flows there. Filled with all the
hope, the madness and the passion of our youth it flows
there, in the daytime, in the dark, drinking with ceaseless glut the land, mining into its tides the earth as it
mines the hours and moments of our life into its tides,
moving against the sides of ships, foaming about piled
crustings of old wharves, sliding like time and silence
by the vast cliff of the city, girdling the stony isle of
life with moving waters—thick with the wastes of earth,
dark with our stains, and heavied with our dumpings,
rich, rank, beautiful, and unending as all life, all living,
as it flows by us, by us, by us, to the sea!

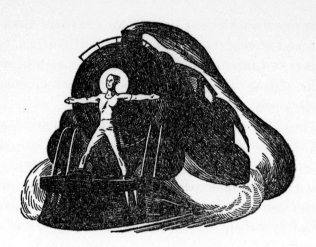

Escape Into the World

THEN the locomotive drew in upon them, loomed enormously above them, and slowly swept by them with a terrific drive of eight-locked pistoned wheels, all higher than their heads, a savage furnace-flare of heat, a hard hose-thick hiss of steam, a moment's vision of a lean old head, an old gloved hand of cunning on the throttle, a glint of demon hawk-eyes fixed forever on the rails, a huge tangle of gauges, levers, valves, and throttles, and the goggled blackened face of the fireman, lit by an intermittent hell of flame, as he bent and swayed with rhythmic swing of laden shovel at his furnace doors.

The locomotive passed above them, darkening the sunlight from their faces, engulfing them at once and filling them with terror, drawing the souls out through their mouths with the God-head of its instant absoluteness, and leaving them there, emptied, frightened, fixed forever, a cluster of huddled figures, a bough of small white staring faces, upturned, silent, and submissive, small, lonely, and afraid.

Then as the heavy rust-black coaches rumbled past, and the wheels ground slowly to a halt, the boy could see his mother's white stunned face beside him, the naked startled innocence of her eyes, and feel her rough worn clasp upon his arm, and hear her startled voice, full of apprehension, terror, and surprise, as she said sharply:

"Hah? What say? Is this his train? I thought——"

It was his train and it had come to take him to the strange and secret heart of the great North that he had never known, but whose austere and lonely image, whose frozen heat and glacial fire, and dark stern beauty had blazed in his vision since he was a child. For he had dreamed and hungered for the proud unknown North with that wild ecstasy, that intolerable and wordless joy of longing and desire, which only a Southerner can feel. With a heart of fire, a brain possessed, a spirit haunted by the strange, secret and unvisited magic of the proud North, he had always known that some day he should find it—his heart's hope and his father's country, the lost but unforgotten half of his own soul,—and take it for his own.

And now that day had come, and these two images—call them rather lights and weathers of man's soul—of the world-far, lost and lonely South, and the fierce, the splendid, strange and secret North, were swarming like a madness through his blood. And just as he had seen a thousand images of the buried and silent South which he had known all his life, so now he had a vision of the proud fierce North with all its shining cities, and its tides of life. He saw the rocky sweetness of its soil and its green loveliness, and he knew its numb soft prescience, its entrail-stirring ecstasy of coming snow, its smell of harbors and its traffic of proud ships.

He could not utter what he wished to say and yet the wild and powerful music of those two images kept swelling in him and it seemed that the passion of their song must burst his heart, explode the tenement of bright blood and agony in which they surged, and tear the sinews of his life asunder unless he found some means to utter them.

But no words came. He knew only the image of man's loneliness, a feeling of sorrow, desolation, and wild mournful secret joy, longing and desire, as sultry, moveless and mysterious in its slow lust as the great rivers of the South themselves. And at the same moment that he felt this wild and mournful sorrow, the slow, hot, secret pulsings of desire, and breathed the heavy and mysterious fragrance of the lost South again, he felt suddenly and terribly, its wild strange pull, the fatal absoluteness of its world-lost resignation.

Then, with a sudden feeling of release, a realization of the incredible escape that now impended for him, he knew that he was waiting for the train, and that the great life of the North, the road to freedom, solitude and the enchanted promise of the golden cities was now before him. Like a dream made real, a magic come to life, he knew that in another hour he would be speeding world-ward, life-ward, North-ward out of the enchanted, time-far hills, out of the dark heart and mournful mystery of the South forever.

And as that overwhelming knowledge came to him, a song of triumph, joy, and victory so savage and unutterable that he could no longer hold it in his heart was torn from his lips in a bestial cry of fury, pain, and ecstasy. He struck his arms out in the shining air for loss, for agony, for joy. The whole earth reeled about him in a kaleidoscopic blur of shining rail, massed heavy greens, and white empetalled faces of the staring people.

Young, and Drunk, and Twenty

IMMORTAL drunkenness! What tribute can we ever
pay, what song can we ever sing, what swelling
praise can ever be sufficient to express the joy, the
gratefulness, and the love which we, who have
known youth and hunger in America, have owed to
alcohol?

We are so lost, so lonely, so forsaken in America:
immense and savage skies bend over us, and we have no
door.

But you, immortal drunkenness, came to us in our
youth when all our hearts were sick with hopelessness,
our spirts maddened with unknown terrors, and our
heads bowed down with nameless shame. You came to
us victoriously, to possess us, and to fill our lives with
your wild music, to make the goat-cry burst from our
exultant throats, to make us know that here upon the
wilderness, the savage land, that here beneath immense,
inhuman skies of time, in all the desolation of the cities,
the gray unceasing flood-tides of the manswarm, our
youth would soar to fortune, fame and love, our
spirits quicken with the power of mighty poetry, our

work go on triumphantly to fulfilment until our lives prevailed.

What does it matter then if since that time of your first coming, magic drunkenness, our head has grown bald, our young limbs heavy, and if our flesh has lain battered, bleeding in the stews?

You came to us with music, poetry, and wild joy when we were twenty, when we reeled home at night through the old moon-whitened streets of Boston and heard our friend, our comrade, and our dead companion, shout through the silence of the moonwhite square: "You are a poet and the world is yours."

And victory, joy, wild hope, and swelling certitude and tenderness surged through the conduits of our blood as we heard that drunken cry, and triumph, glory, proud belief was resting like a chrysm around us as we heard that cry, and turned our eyes then to the moon-drunk skies of Boston, knowing only that we were young, and drunk, and twenty, and that the power of mighty poetry was within us, and the glory of the great earth lay before us—because we were young and drunk and twenty, and could never die!

Dreams of Guilt and Time

THERE was a kind of dream which I can only
summarize as dreams of Guilt and Time.
Chameleon-like in all their damnable and unending fecundities, they restored to me the
whole huge world that I had known, the billion faces
and the million tongues, and they restored it to me
with the malevolent triumph of a passive and unwanted
ease. My daily conflict with Amount and Number, the
huge accumulations of my years of struggle with the
forms of life, my brutal and unending efforts to record
upon my memory each brick and paving stone of every
street that I had ever walked upon, each face of every
thronging crowd in every city, every country, with which
my spirit had contested its savage and uneven struggle for supremacy—they all returned now—each stone,

each street, each town, each country—yes, even every book in the library whose loaded shelves I had tried vainly to devour at college—they returned upon the wings of these mighty, sad, and somehow quietly demented dreams—I saw and heard and knew them all at once, was instantly without pain or anguish, with the calm consciousness of God, master of the whole universe of life against whose elements I had contended vainly for all-knowledge for so many years. And the fruit of that enormous triumph, the calm and instant passivity of that inhuman and demented immortality, was somehow sadder and more bitter than the most galling bitterness of defeat in my contention with the multitudes of life had ever been.

For above that universe of dreams there shone forever a tranquil, muted, and unchanging light of time. And through the traffic of those thronging crowds— whose faces, whose whole united and divided life was now instantly and without an effort of the will my *own*—there rose forever the sad unceasing murmurs of the body of this life, the vast recessive fadings of the shadow of man's death that breathes forever with its dirge-like sigh around the huge shores of the world.

And *beyond, beyond*—forever *above, around, behind* the vast and tranquil consciousness of my spirit that now held the earth and all her elements in the huge clasp of its effortless subjection—there dwelt forever the fatal knowledge of my own inexpiable *guilt*.

I did not know what I had done—I only knew that I had ruinously forgotten time, and by so doing had

betrayed my brother men. I had been long from home
—why, how, or in what way, I could not know—but
drugged there in the drowsy fumes of some green country of the witches' magic, with something in me dark
and full of grief I could not quite remember. And
suddenly I was home again—walking alone beneath
that light of tranquil, quiet, and unchanging brown,
walking the roads, the hill-slopes, and the streets of
my familiar country—sometimes the *exact* and *actual*
lineaments of home, my childhood, and my native
town, so that not only all that I had known and remembered—each familiar street and face and house
and every cobblestone upon the pavement—but countless things I never knew that I had seen, or had forgotten that I ever knew—a rusty hinge upon the cellar
door, the way a stair creaked, an old cracked blister
of brown paint upon the woodwork by the grate, an
oak tree trunk upon the hill all hollowed out upon one
side by a knotted hole, the glazed pattern of the glass
in the front door, the brass handle of a street-car brake-
control, quite rubbed to silver on one side by the hard
grip of the motorman, and covered by a cloth tobacco
sack—such things as these, together with a million
others, returned now to torment my sleep.

And even more than these, more, more familiar even
than these scenes of memory and inheritance, were those
landscapes that somehow had been *derived* from them
—the streets, the towns, the houses and the faces that I
saw and imagined not the way they *were,* but the way
they *should* be in the unfathomed, strange, and unsus-

spected logics of man's brain and heart—and that were, on this account, more real than real-ness, and more true than home.

I had been long from home—I had grown old in some evil and enchanted place, I had allowed my life to waste and rot in the slothful and degrading surfeits of Circean time. And now my life was lost—my work undone—I had betrayed my home, my friends, my people, in the duties of some solemn and inviolable trust—and suddenly I was home again, and *silence* was my answer!

They did not look at me with looks of bitterness and hate, they did not lash me with the fierce opprobrium of scorn, or curse me with the menaces of vengeance and reprisal—oh, if they had, what balm of anguish and of judgment even curses would have had!—but instead their look was silence, and their tongue was mute. And again, again, I walked the streets of that familiar town, and after years of absence saw again the features of familiar faces, and heard familiar words, the sounds of well-known voices once again, and with a still and deep amazement saw the shift and interplay of action, the common familiarity of day, the traffic of the streets, and saw that it was all as it had always been, I had forgotten nothing—until I passed them, and death fell.

I walked among them, and their movements ceased, I walked among them, and their tongues were still, I walked among them and they neither moved nor spoke until I passed, and if they looked at me, their eyes were

blank with silence and no memory; there was no re-
proach, no grief, and no contempt, there was no bitterness and scorn—if I had died, there should at least have
been the ghost of memory, but it was as if I never had
been born. And so I passed them by, and everywhere
I trod was death, and when I had gone by, behind me
I could hear their voices start again; the clamours of the
street, and all the traffic of bright day awoke—but only
after I had passed them by!

And so the whole town flowed around me, was behind
me, and at once, without a bridge or instant of transition, I was walking on a barren road, across the huge
sweep of a treeless waste and barren vacancy, and that
tranquil, sad and fatal light shone on me from the horror of a planetary vacancy, the lidless and remorseless
eye of an unperturbed sky that ate into my naked spirit
constantly the acid of unuttered shame.

The Four Lost Men

GARFIELD, Arthur, Harrison, and Hayes—time
of my father's time, blood of his blood, life of
his life, had been living, real, and actual people in all the passion, power, and feeling of
my father's youth. And for me they were the lost Amer-

icans: their gravely vacant and bewhiskered faces mixed, melted, swam together in the sea-depths of a past intangible, immeasurable, and unknowable as the buried city of Persepolis.

And they were lost.

For who was Garfield, martyred man, and who had seen him in the streets of life? Who could believe his footfalls ever sounded on a lonely pavement? Who had heard the casual and familiar tones of Chester Arthur? And where was Harrison? Where was Hayes? Which had the whiskers, which the burnsides: which was which?

Were they not lost?

Into their ears, as ours, the tumults of forgotten crowds, upon their brains the million printings of lost time, and suddenly upon their dying sight the brief bitter pain and joy of a few death-bright, fixed and fading memories: the twisting of a leaf upon a bough, the grinding felloe-rim against the curb, the long, distant and retreating thunder of a train upon the rails.

Garfield, Hayes, and Harrison were Ohio men; but only the name of Garfield had been brightened by his blood. But at night had they not heard the howlings of demented wind, the sharp, clean, windy raining to the earth of acorns? Had all of them not walked down lonely roads at night in winter and seen a light and known it was theirs? Had all of them not known the wilderness?

Had they not known the smell of old bound calf and

well-worn leathers, the Yankee lawyer's smell of strong
tobacco spit and courthouse urinals, the smell of horses,
harness, hay, and sweating country men, of jury rooms
and court rooms—the strong male smell of Justice at the
county seat, and heard a tap along dark corridors where
fell a drop in darkness with a punctual crescent monotone of time, dark time?

Had not Garfield, Hayes, and Harrison studied law
in offices with a dark brown smell? Had not the horses
trotted past below their windows in wreaths of dust
along a straggling street of shacks and buildings with
false fronts? Had they not heard below them the voices
of men talking, loitering up in drawling heat? Had they
not heard the casual, rich-fibered, faintly howling country voices, and heard the rustling of a woman's skirt,
and waiting silence, slyly lowered tones of bawdry and
then huge guffaws, slapped meaty thighs, and high fat
choking laughter? And in the dusty dozing heat, while
time buzzed slowly, like a fly, had not Garfield, Arthur,
Harrison, and Hayes then smelled the river, the humid,
subtly fresh, half-rotten river, and thought of the white
flesh of the women then beside the river, and felt a slow
impending passion in their entrails, a heavy rending
power in their hands?

Then Garfield, Arthur, Harrison, and Hayes had
gone to war, and each became a brigadier or major-
general. All were bearded men: they saw a spattering
of bright blood upon the leaves, and they heard the
soldiers talking in the dark of food and women. They
held the bridge-head in bright dust at places with such

names as Wilson's Mill and Spangler's Run, and their men smashed cautiously through dense undergrowth. And they had heard the surgeons cursing after battles, and the little rasp of saws. They had seen boys standing awkwardly holding their entrails in their hands, and pleading pitifully with fear-bright eyes: "Is it bad, General? Do you think it's bad?"

When the canister came through it made a ragged hole. It smashed through tangled leaves and boughs, sometimes it plunked solidly into the fiber of a tree. Sometimes when it struck a man it tore away the roof of his brain, the wall of his skull, raggedly, so that his brains seethed out upon a foot of wilderness, and the blood blackened and congealed, and he lay there in his thick clumsy uniform, with a smell of urine in the wool, in the casual, awkward, and incompleted attitude of sudden death. And when Garfield, Arthur, Harrison, and Hayes saw these things they saw that it was not like the picture they had had, as children, it was not like the works of Walter Scott and William Gillmore Sims. They saw that the hole was not clean and small and in the central front, and the field was not green nor fenced, nor mown. Over the vast and immemorable earth the quivering heated light of afternoon was shining, a field swept rudely upward to a lift of rugged wood, and field by field, gulley by gulch by fold, the earth advanced in rude, sweet, limitless convolutions.

Then Garfield, Arthur, Harrison, and Hayes had paused by the bridge-head for a moment and were still, seeing the bright blood at noon upon the trampled wheat, feeling the brooding hush of six o'clock across the fields where all the storming feet had passed at dawn, seeing the way the rough field hedge leaned out across the dusty road, the casual intrusions of the coarse field grasses and the hot dry daisies to the edges of the road, seeing the rock-bright shallows of the creek, the sweet cool shade and lean of river trees across the water.

They paused then by the bridge-head looking at the water. They saw the stark blank flatness of the old red mill that somehow was like sunset, coolness, sorrow, and delight, and looking at the faces of dead boys among the wheat, the most-oh-most familiar-plain, the death-strange faces of the dead Americans, they stood there for a moment, thinking, feeling, thinking, with strong, wordless wonder in their hearts:

"As we leaned on the sills of evening, as we stood in the frames of the marvellous doors, as we were received into silence, the flanks of the slope and the slanted light, as we saw the strange hushed shapes upon the land, the muted distances, knowing all things then —what could we say except that all our comrades were spread quietly around us and that noon was far?

"What can we say now of the lonely land—what can we say now of the deathless shapes and substances— what can we say who have lived here with our lives, bone, blood, and brain, and all our tongueless languages, hearing on many a casual road the plain-familiar voices of Americans, and who to-morrow will be buried in the earth, knowing the fields will steep to silence after us, the slant light deepen on the slopes, and peace and

evening will come back again—at one now with the million shapes and single substance of our land, at one with
evening, peace, the huge stride of the undulant oncoming night, at one, also, with morning?

"Silence receive us, and the field of peace, hush of
the measureless land, the unabated distances; shape of
the one and single substance and the million forms, re-
plenish us, restore us, and unite us with your vast images
of quietness and joy. Stride of the undulant night, come
swiftly now; engulf us, silence, in your great-starred
secrecy; speak to our hearts of stillness, for we have,
save this, no speech.

"There is the bridge we crossed, the mill we slept in,
and the creek. There is a field of wheat, a hedge, a
dusty road, an apple orchard, and the sweet wild tangle
of a wood upon that hill. And there is six o'clock across
the fields again, now and always, as it was and will
be to world's end forever. And some of us have died
this morning coming through the field—and that was
time—time—time. We shall not come again, we never
shall come back again, we never shall come back along
this road again as we did once at morning—so, brothers,
let us look again before we go. . . . There is the mill,
and there the hedge, and there the shallows of the rock-
bright waters of the creek, and there the sweet and
most familiar coolness of the trees—and surely we have
been this way before!" they cried.

"Oh, surely, brothers, we have sat upon the bridge,
before the mill, and sung together by the rock-bright
waters of the creek at evening, and come across the

wheatfield in the morning and heard the dew-sweet bird-song rising from the hedge before! You plain, oh-most-familiar and most homely earth, proud earth of this huge land unutterable, proud nobly swelling earth, in all your delicacy, wildness, savagery, and terror—grand earth in all your loneliness, beauty and wild joy, terrific earth in all your limitless fecundities, swelling with infinite fold and convolution into the reaches of the West forever—American earth!—bridge, hedge, and creek and dusty road—you plain tremendous poetry of Wilson's Mill, where boys died in the wheat this morning—you unutterable far-near, strange-familiar, homely earth of magic, for which a word would do if we could find it, for which a word would do if we could call it by its name, for which a word would do that never can be spoken, that can never be forgotten, and that will never be revealed—oh, proud, familiar, nobly swelling earth, it seems we must have known you before! It seems we must have known you forever, but all we know for certain is that we came along this road one time at morning, and now our blood is painted on the wheat, and you are ours now, we are yours forever—and there is something here we never shall remember—there is something here we never shall forget!"

Had Garfield, Arthur, Harrison, and Hayes been young? Or had they all been born with flowing whiskers, sideburns, and wing collars, speaking gravely from the cradle of their mother's arms the noble vacant sonorities of far-seeing statesmanship? It could not be.

Had they not all been young men in the 'Thirties, the 'Forties, and the 'Fifties? Did they not, as we, cry out at night along deserted roads into demented winds? Did they not, as we, cry out in ecstasy and exultancy, as the full measure of their hunger, their potent and inchoate hope, went out into that single wordless cry?

Did they not, as we, when young, prowl softly up and down in the dark hours of the night, seeing the gas-lamps flare and flutter on the corner, falling with livid light upon the corners of old cobbled streets of brown-stone houses? Had they not heard the lonely rhythmic clopping of a horse, the jounting wheels of a hansom cab, upon those barren cobbles? And had they not waited, trembling in the darkness, till the horse and cab had passed, had vanished with the lonely recession of shod hoofs, and then were heard no more?

And then had Garfield, Arthur, Harrison, and Hayes not waited, waited in the silence of the night, prowling up and down the lonely cobbled street, with trembling lips, numb entrails, pounding hearts? Had they not set their jaws, made sudden indecisive movements, felt terror, joy, a numb impending ecstasy, and waited, waited then—for what? Had they not waited, hearing sounds of shifting engines in the yards at night, hearing the hoarse, gaseous breaths of little engines through the grimy fan-flare of their funnels? Had they not waited there in that dark street with the fierce lone hunger of a boy, feeling around them the immense and moving quietness of sleep, the heartbeats of ten thousand sleeping men, as they waited, waited in the night?

Had they not, as we, then turned their eyes up and seen the huge starred visage of the night, the immense and lilac darkness of America in April? Had they not heard the sudden, shrill, and piping whistle of a departing engine? Had they not waited, thinking, feeling, seeing then the immense mysterious continent of night, the wild and lyric earth, so casual, sweet, and strange-familiar, in all its space and savagery and terror, its mystery and joy, its limitless sweep and rudeness, its delicate and savage fecundity? Had they not had a vision of the plains, the mountains, and the rivers flowing in the darkness, the huge pattern of the everlasting earth and the all-engulfing wilderness of America?

Had they not felt, as we have felt, as they waited in the night, the huge, lonely earth of night-time and America, on which ten thousand lonely sleeping little towns were strewn? Had they not seen the fragile network of light, racketing, ill-joined little rails across the land, over which the lonely little trains rushed on in darkness, flinging a handful of lost echoes at the river's edge, leaving an echo in the cut's resounding cliff, and being engulfed then in huge lonely night, in all-brooding, all-engulfing night? Had they not known, as we have known, the wild secret joy and mystery of the everlasting earth, the lilac dark, the savage, silent, all-possessing wilderness that gathered in around ten thousand lonely little towns, ten million lost and lonely sleepers, and waited, and abode forever, and was still?

Had not Garfield, Arthur, Harrison, and Hayes then

waited, feeling wild joy and sorrow in their hearts, and a savage hunger and desire—a flame, a fire, a fury—burning fierce and lean and lonely in the night, burning forever while the sleepers slept? Were they not burning, burning, burning, even as the rest of us have burned? Were Garfield, Arthur, Harrison, and Hayes not burning in the night? Were they not burning forever in the silence of the little towns, with all the fierce hunger, savage passion, limitless desire that young men in this land have known in the darkness?

Had Garfield, Arthur, Harrison, and Hayes not waited then, as we have waited, with numb lips and pounding hearts and fear, delight, strong joy and terror stirring in their entrails as they stood in the silent street before a house, proud, evil, lavish, lighted—certain, secret, and alone? And as they heard the hoof, the wheel, the sudden whistle and the immense and sleeping silence of the town, did they not wait there in the darkness, thinking:

"Oh, there are new lands, morning, and a shining city. Soon, soon, soon!"

Did not Garfield, Arthur, Harrison, and Hayes, those fierce and jubilant young men, who waited there, as we have waited, in the silent barren street, with trembling lips, numb hands, with terror, savage joy, fierce rapture alive and stirring in their entrails—did they not feel, as we have felt, when they heard the shrill departing warning of the whistle in the dark, the sound of great wheels pounding at the river's edge? Did they not feel, as we have felt, as they waited there in the intolerable sweetness, wilderness, mystery, and terror of the great earth in the month of April, and knew themselves alone, alive and young and mad and secret with desire and hunger in the great sleep-silence of the night, the impending, cruel, all-promise of this land? Were they not torn, as we have been, by sharp pain and wordless lust, the asp of time, the thorn of spring, the sharp, the tongueless cry? Did they not say:

"Oh, there are women in the East—and new lands, morning, and a shining city! There are forgotten fume-flaws of bright smoke above Manhattan, the forest of masts about the crowded isle, the proud cleavages of departing ships, the soaring web, the wing-like swoop and joy of the great bridge, and men with derby hats who come across the bridge to greet us—come, brothers, let us go to find them all! For the huge murmur of the city's million-footed life, far, bee-like, drowsy, strange as time, has come to haunt our ears with all its golden prophecy of joy and triumph, fortune, happiness and love such as no men before have ever known. Oh, brothers, in the city, in the far-shining, glorious, time-enchanted spell of that enfabled city we shall find great men and lovely women, and unceasingly ten thousand new delights, a thousand magical adventures! We shall wake at morning in our rooms of lavish brown to hear the hoof and wheel upon the city street again, and smell the harbor, fresh, half-rotten, with its bracelet of bright tides, its traffic of proud sea-borne ships, its purity and joy of dancing morning-gold.

"Street of the day, with the unceasing promise of

your million-footed life, we come to you!" they cried. "Street of the thunderous wheels at noon, street of the great parades of marching men, the band's bright oncoming blare, the brave stick-candy whippings of a flag, street of the cries and shouts, the swarming feet, —street of the jounting cabs, the ringing hooves, the horse-cars and the jingling bells, the in-horse ever bending its sad nodding head toward its lean and patient comrade on the right—great street of furious life and movement, noon, and joyful labors, your image blazes in our hearts forever, and we come!

"Street of the morning, street of hope!" they cried. "Street of coolness, slanted light, the frontal cliff and gulch of steep blue shade, street of the dancing morning-gold of waters on the flashing tides, street of the rusty weathered slips, the blunt-nosed ferry foaming in with its packed wall of small white staring faces, all silent and intent, all turned toward *you*—proud street! Street of the pungent sultry smells of new-ground coffee, the good green smell of money, the fresh half-rotten harbor smell with all its evocation of your mast-bound harbor and its tide of ships, great street!—Street of the old buildings grimed richly with the warm and mellow dinginess of trade—street of the million morning feet forever hurrying onward in the same direction—proud street of hope and joy and morning, in your steep canyon we shall win the wealth, the fame, the power and the esteem which our lives and talents merit!

"Street of the night!" they cried, "great street of mystery and suspense, terror and delight, eagerness and hope, street edged forever with the dark menace of impending joy, an unknown happiness and fulfilment, street of gaiety, warmth, and evil, street of the great hotels, the lavish bars and restaurants, and the softly golden glow, the fading lights and empetalled whiteness of a thousand hushed white thirsty faces in the crowded theatres, street of the tidal flood of faces, lighted with your million lights and all thronging, tireless and unquenched in their insatiate searching after pleasure, street of the lovers coming along with slow steps, their faces turned toward each other, lost in the oblivion of love among the everlasting web and weaving of the crowd, street of the white face, the painted mouth, the shining and inviting eye—oh, street of night, with all your mystery, joy, and terror—we have thought of you, proud street.

"And we shall move at evening in the noiseless depths of sumptuous carpets, through all the gaiety, warmth, and brilliant happiness of great lighted chambers of the night, filled with the mellow thrum and languor of the violins, and where the loveliest and most desirable women in the world—the beloved daughters of great merchants, bankers, millionaires, or rich young widows, beautiful, loving, and alone—are moving with a slow proud undulance, a look of depthless tenderness in their fragile, lovely faces. And the loveliest of them all," they cried, "is ours, is ours forever, if we want her! For, brothers, in the city, in the far-shining, magic, golden city, we shall move among great men and glorious women and know nothing but strong joy and happiness forever, winning by our courage, talent, and deserving, the highest and most honored place in the most fortunate and happy life that men have known, if only we will go and make it ours!"

So thinking, feeling, waiting as we have waited in the sleeping silence of the night in silent streets, hearing, as we have heard, the sharp blast of the warning whistle, the thunder of great wheels upon the river's edge, feeling, as we have felt, the mystery of nighttime and of April, the huge impending presence, the wild and secret promise, of the savage, lonely, everlasting earth, finding, as we have found, no doors to enter, and being torn, as we were torn, by the thorn of spring, the sharp, the wordless cry, did they not carry—these young men of the past, Garfield, Arthur, Harrison, and Hayes—even as we have carried, within their little tenements of bone, blood, sinew, sweat, and agony, the intolerable burden of all the pain, joy, hope and savage hunger that a man can suffer, that the world can know?

Were they not lost? Were they not lost, as all of us have been who have known youth and hunger in this land, and who have waited, lean and mad and lonely in the night, and who have found no goal, no wall, no dwelling, and no door?

The years flow by like water, and one day it is spring again. Shall we ever ride out of the gates of the East again, as we did once at morning, and seek again, as we did then, new lands, the promise of the war, and glory, joy, and triumph, and a shining city?

O youth, still wounded, living, feeling with a woe unutterable, still grieving with a grief intolerable, still thirsting with a thirst unquenchable—where are we to seek? For the wild tempest breaks above us, the wild fury beats about us, the wild hunger feeds upon us— and we are houseless, doorless, unassuaged, and driven on forever; and our brains are mad, our hearts are wild and wordless, and we cannot speak.

Faces

HEALTH was to be found in the steady stare of the cats and dogs, or in the smooth vacant chops of the peasant. But he looked on the faces of the lords of the earth—and he saw them wasted and devoured by the beautiful disease of thought and passion. In the pages of a thousand books he saw their portraits: Coleridge at twenty-five, with the loose sensual mouth, gaping idiotically, the vast staring eyes, holding in their opium depths the vision of seas haunted by the albatross, the great white forehead—head mixed of Zeus and the village degenerate; the lean worn head of Cæsar, a little thirsty in the flanks; and the dreaming mummy face of Kublai Khan, lit with eyes that flickered with green fires. And he saw the faces of the great Thothmes, and Aspalta and Mycerinus, and all the heads of subtle Egypt—those smooth unwrinkled faces that held the wisdom of 1200 gods. And the strange wild faces of the Goth, the Frank, the Vandal, that came storming up below the old tired eyes of Rome. And the weary craftiness on the face of the great Jew, Disraeli; the terrible skull-grin of Voltaire; the mad ranting savagery of Ben Jonson's; the dour wild agony of Carlyle's; and the faces of Heine, and Rousseau, and Dante, and Tiglath-Pileser, and Cervantes—these were all faces on which life had fed. They were faces wasted by the vulture, Thought; they were faces seared and hollowed by the flame of Beauty.

What Is This Memory?

ALL through the wintry afternoon the great train rushed down across Bavaria. Swiftly and powerfully it gathered motion, it left the last scattered outposts of the city behind it, and swift as dreams the train was rushing out across the level plain surrounding Munich.

The day was gray, the sky impenetrable and somewhat heavy, and yet filled with a strong clean Alpine vigor, with that odorless and yet exultant energy of cold mountain air. Within an hour the train had entered Alpine country, now there were hills, valleys, the immediate sense of soaring ranges, and the dark enchantment of the forests of Germany, those forests which are something more than trees—which are a spell, a magic, and a sorcery, filling the hearts of men, and particularly those strangers who have some racial kinship with that land, with a dark music, a haunting memory, never wholly to be captured.

It is an overwhelming feeling of immediate and impending discovery, such as men might have who come for the first time to their father's country. It is like coming to that unknown land for which our spirits long so passionately in youth, which is the dark side of our soul, the strange brother and the complement of the land we have known in our childhood. And it is revealed to us instantly the moment that we see it, with a powerful emotion of perfect recognition and disbelief, with that dream-like reality of strangeness and familiarity which dreams and all enchantment have.

What is it? What is this wild fierce joy and sorrow swelling in our hearts? What is this memory that we cannot phrase, this instant recognition for which we have no words? We cannot say. We have no way to give it utterance, no ordered evidence to give it proof, and scornful pride can mock us for a superstitious folly. Yet we will know the dark land at the very moment that we come to it, and though we have no tongue, no proof, no utterance for what we feel, we have what we have, we know what we know, we are what we are.

And what are we? We are the naked men, the lost Americans. Immense and lonely skies bend over us, ten thousand men are marching in our blood. Where does it come from—the sense of strangeness, instant recognition, the dream-haunted, almost captured, memory? Where does it come from, the constant hunger and the rending lust, and the music, dark and solemn, elfish, magic, sounding through the wood? How is it that this boy, who is American, has known this strange land from the first moment that he saw it?

How is it that from his first night in a German town he has understood the tongue he never heard before, has spoken instantly, saying all he wished to say, in a strange language which he could not speak, speaking a weird argot which was neither his nor theirs, of which he was not even conscious, so much did it seem to be the spirit of a language, not the words, he spoke, and instantly, in this fashion, understood by every one with whom he talked?

No. He could not prove it, yet he knew that it was there, buried deep in the brain and blood of man, the utter knowledge of this land and of his father's people. He had felt it all, the tragic and insoluble admixture of the race. He knew the terrible fusion of the brute and of the spirit. He knew the nameless fear of the old barbaric forest, the circle of barbaric figures gathered round him in their somber and unearthly ring, the sense of drowning in the blind forest horrors of barbaric time. He carried all within himself, the slow gluttony and lust of the unsated swine, as well as the strange and powerful music of the soul.

He knew the hatred and revulsion from the never-sated beast—the beast with the swine-face and the quenchless thirst, the never-ending hunger, the thick, slow, rending hand that fumbled with a smouldering and unsated lust. And he hated the great beast with the hate of hell and murder because he felt and knew it in himself and was himself the prey of its rending, quenchless, and obscene desires. Rivers of wine to drink, whole roast oxen turning on the spit, and through the forest murk, the roaring wall of huge beast-bodies and barbaric sound about him, the lavish flesh of the great blonde women, in brutal orgy of the all-devouring, never-sated maw of the huge belly, without end or surfeit—all was mixed into his blood, his spirit, and his life.

It had been given to him somehow from the dark time-horror of the ancient forest together with all that was magical, glorious, strange and beautiful: the husky horn-notes sounding faint and elfin through the forests, the infinite strange weavings, dense mutations of the old Germanic soul of man. How cruel, baffling, strange, and sorrowful was the enigma of the race: the power and strength of the incorruptible and soaring spirit rising from the huge corrupted beast with such a radiant purity, and the powerful enchantments of grand music, noble poetry, so sorrowfully and unalterably woven and inwrought with all the blind brute hunger of the belly and the beast of man.

It was all his, and all contained in his one life. And it could, he knew, never be distilled out of him, no more than one can secrete from his flesh his father's blood, the ancient and immutable weavings of dark time. And for this reason, as he now looked out the window of the train at that lonely Alpine land of snow and dark enchanted forest he felt the sense of familiar recognition instantly, the feeling that he had always known this place, that it was home. And something dark, wild, jubilant, and strange was exulting, swelling in his spirit like a grand and haunting music heard in dreams.

To Keep Time With

TIME, please, time. . . . What time is it? . . . Gentlemen, it's closing time. . . . Time, gentlemen . . . that time of year thou may'st in me behold. . . . In the good old summer-time. . . . I keep thinking of you all the time . . . all the time . . . and all the time. . . . A long time ago the world began. . . . There goes the last bell, run, boy, run: you'll just have time. . . . There are times that make you ha-a-ap-py, there are times that make you sa-a-ad. . . . Do you remember the night you came back to the University?: it was that time right after your brother's death, you had just come back that night, I know I was coming across the campus before Old East when I saw you coming up the path with a suitcase in your hand. It was raining but we both stopped and began to talk there—we stepped in under one of the oak-trees because it was raining. I can still remember the old, wet, shining bark of the tree—the reason I can remember is that you put your hand out and leaned against the tree as you talked to me and I kept thinking how tall you were— of course you didn't notice it, you weren't conscious of it but you had your head up and it must have been about

eight feet above the ground. But I can remember everything we said that night—it was that time when you
came back just after your brother's death: that's when
it was all right, I guess that's why I can remember it so
well. . . . It's time all little boys were in bed. . . .
Now, boy, I'll tell you when it was: it was that time
your Papa made that trip to California—the reason that
I know is I had just got a letter from him that morning
written from Los Angeles telling me how he had seen
John Balch and old Professor Truman, and how they
had both gone into the real-estate business out there,
and both of them getting rich by leaps and bounds—
but that's just exactly when it was, sir, the time he made
that trip out there in 1906, along towards the end of
February, and I had just finished reading his letter
when—well as I say now . . . Garfield, Arthur, Harrison and Hayes . . . time of my father's time, life of
his life. "Ah, Lord," he said, "I knew them all—and all
of them are gone. I'm the only one that's left. By God,
I'm getting old." . . . In the year that the locusts
came, something that happened in the year the locusts
came, two voices that I heard there in that year. . . .
Child! Child! It seems so long ago since the year the
locusts came, and all of the trees were eaten bare: so
much has happened, and it seems so long ago. . . .

"To keep time with!"—To Eugene Gant, Presented
to Him on the Occasion of His Twelfth Birthday, by
His Brother, B. H. Gant, Oct. 3, 1912. . . . "To keep
time with!" . . . Up on the mountain, down in the
valley, deep, deep in the hill, Ben, cold, cold, cold.

Speaking Dust

WHOEVER builds a bridge across this earth," they cried, "whoever lays a rail across this mouth, whoever stirs the dust where these bones lie, let him go dig them up, and say his Hamlet to the engineers. Son, son," their voices said, "is the earth richer where our own earth lay? Must you untwist the vine-root from the buried heart? Have you unrooted mandrake from our brains? Or the rich flowers, the big rich flowers, the strange unknown flowers?

"You must admit the grass is thicker here. Hair grew like April on our buried flesh. These men were full of juice, you'll grow good corn here, golden wheat. The men are dead, you say? They may be dead, but you'll grow trees here; you'll grow an oak but we were richer than an oak; you'll grow a plum tree here that's bigger than an oak, it will be all filled with plums as big as little apples.

"We were great men and mean men hated us," they said. "We were all men who cried out when we were hurt, wept when we were sad, drank, ate, were strong, weak, full of fear, were loud and full of clamor, yet grew quiet when dark came. Fools laughed at us and witlings sneered at us: how could they know our brains were subtler than a snake's? Because they were more small, were they more delicate? Did their pale sapless flesh sense things too fine for our imagining? How can you think it, child? Our hearts were wrought more strangely than a cat's, full of deep twistings, woven sinews, flushing with dull and brilliant fires; and our marvellous nerves, flame-tipped, crossed wires too intricate for their fathoming.

"What could they see," the voices rose above the sound of the wheels, with their triumphant boast, "what could they know of men like us, whose fathers hewed the stone above their graves, and now lie under mountains, plains, and forests, hills of granite, drowned by a flooding river, killed by the stroke of the everlasting earth? Now only look where these men have been buried: they've heaved their graves up in great laughing lights of flowers—do you see other flowers so rich on other graves?

"Who sows the barren earth?" their voices cried. "We sowed the wilderness with blood and sperm. Three hundred of your blood and bone are recompacted with the native earth: we gave a tongue to solitude, a pulse to the desert, the barren earth received us and gave back our agony: we made the earth cry out. One lies in Oregon, and one, by a broken wheel and horse's skull, still grips a gunstock on the Western trail. Another one has helped to make Virginia richer. One died at Chancellorsville in Union blue, and one at Shiloh walled with Yankee dead. Another was ripped open in a bar-room brawl and walked three blocks to find a doctor, holding his entrails thoughtfully in his hands.

"One died in Pennsylvania reaching for a fork: her reach was greater than her grasp; she fell, breaking her hip, cut off from red rare beef and roasting-ears at ninety-six. Another whored and preached his way from Hatteras to the Golden Gate: he preached milk and honey for the kidneys, sassafras for jaundice, sulphur for uric acid, slippery-ellum for decaying gums, spinach for the goitre, rhubarb for gnarled joints and all the twistings of rheumatism, and pure spring water mixed with vinegar for that great ailment dear to Venus, that makes the world and Frenchmen kin. He preached the brotherhood and love of man, the coming of Christ and Armageddon by the end of 1886, and he founded the Sons of Abel, the Daughters of Ruth, the Children of The Pentateuch, as well as twenty other sects; and finally he died at eighty-four, a son of the Lord, a prophet, and a saint.

"Two hundred more are buried in the hills of home: these men got land, fenced it, owned it, tilled it; they traded in wood, stone, cotton, corn, tobacco; they built houses, roads, grew trees and orchards. Wherever these men went, they got land and worked it, built upon it, farmed it, sold it, added to it. These men were hill-born and hill-haunted: all knew the mountains, but few knew the sea.

"So there we are, child, lacking our thousand years and ruined walls, perhaps, but with a glory of our own, laid out across three thousand miles of earth. There have been bird-calls for our flesh within the wilderness. So call, please, call! Call the robin red-breast and the wren, who in dark woods discover the friendless bodies of unburied men!

"Immortal land, cruel and immense as God," they cried, "we shall go wandering on your breast forever! Wherever great wheels carry us is home—home for our hunger, home for all things except the heart's small fence and dwelling-place of love.

"Who sows the barren earth?" they said. "Who needs the land? You'll make great engines yet, and taller towers. And what's a trough of bone against a tower? You need the earth? Whoever needs the earth may have the earth. Our dust, wrought in this land, stirred by its million sounds, will stir and tremble to the passing wheel. Whoever needs the earth may use the earth. Go dig us up and there begin your bridge. But whoever builds a bridge across this earth, whoever lays a rail across this mouth, whoever needs the trench where these bones lie, let him go dig them up and say his Hamlet to the engineers."

Return to America

IMMENSE and sudden, and with the abrupt nearness, the telescopic magic of a dream, the English
ship appeared upon the coasts of France, and ap-
proached with the strange, looming immediacy of
powerful and gigantic objects that move at great speed:

there was no sense of continuous movement, of gradual and progressive enlargement, rather the visages of the ship melted rapidly from one bigness to another as do the visages of men in a cinema, which, by a series of fading sizes, brings these kinematic shapes of things, like genii unstoppered from a wizard's bottle, to an overpowering command above the spectator.

At first there was only the calm endlessness of the evening sea, the worn headlands of Europe, and the land, with its rich, green slopes, its striped patterns of minutely cultivated earth, its ancient fortresses and its town—the town of Cherbourg—which, from this distance, lay like a solid pattern of old chalk at the base of the coastal indentation.

Westward, a little to the south, against the darkening bulk of the headland, a long riband of smoke, black and low, told the position of the ship. She was approaching fast, her bulk widened: she had been a dot, a smudge, a shape—a tiny, hardly noticed point in the calm and immense geography of evening. Now she was there, sliding gently in beyond the ancient breakwater, inhabiting and dominating the universe with the presence of her 60,000 tons, so that the vast setting of sky and sea and earth, in which formerly she had been only an inconspicuous but living mark, were now a background for her magnificence.

At this very moment of her arrival the sun rested upon the western wave like a fading coal: its ancient light fell over sea and land without violence or heat, with a remote, unearthly glow that had the delicate tinging of old bronze. Then, swiftly, the sun sank down into the sea, the uninhabited sky now burned with a fierce, an almost unbearable glory; the sun's old light had faded; and the ship was there outside the harbor, sliding softly through the water now, and quartering, in slow turn, upon the land as she came up for anchor.

The sheer wall of her iron plates scarcely seemed to move at all now in the water, it was as if she were fixed and founded there among the tides, as implacable as the headlands of the coast; yet, over her solid bows the land was wheeling slowly. Water foamed noisily from her sides in thick, tumbling columns: the sea-gulls swarmed around her, fluttering greedily and heavily to the water with their creaking and unearthly clamor. Then her anchors rushed out of her, and she stood still.

Meanwhile, the tenders, bearing the passengers who were going to board the ship, had put out from the town even before the ship's arrival, and were now quite near. They had, in fact, cruised slowly for some time about the outer harbor, for the ship was late and the commander had wirelessed asking that there be as little delay as possible when he arrived.

Now the light faded on the land: the fierce, hard brilliance of the western sky, full of bright gold and ragged flame, had melted to an orange afterglow, the subtle, grapy bloom of dusk was melting across the land; the town, far off, was half immersed in it, its moving shadow stole across the fields and slopes, it moved upon the waters like a weft. Above the land the sky was yet full of light—of that strange, phantasmal light of evening which reveals itself to people standing in the dusk below without touching them with any of its radiance: the material and physical property of light seems to have been withdrawn from it, and it remains briefly in the sky, without substance or any living power, like the ghost of light, its soul, its spirit.

In these late skies of France, this late, evening light of waning summer had in it a quality that was high and sad, remote and full of classic repose and dignity. Beneath it, it was as if one saw people grave and beautiful move slowly homeward through long aisles of planted trees: the light was soft, lucent, delicately empearled—and all great labor was over, all strong joy and hate and love had ended, all wild desire and hope, all maddening of the flesh and heart and brain, the fever and the tumult and the fret; and the grave-eyed women in long robes walked slowly with cut flowers in their arms among the glades of trees, and night had come, and they would go to the wood no more.

Now, in this light, all over the land of France the men were coming from the fields: they had used preciously the last light of day, summer was almost over, the fields were mown, the hay was raked and stacked, and in a thousand places, along the Rhine, and along the Marne, in Burgundy, in Touraine, in Provence, the wains were lumbering slowly down the roads.

In the larger towns the nervous and swarming activity of evening had begun: the terraces of the cafés were uncomfortably crowded with noisy people, the pavements were thronged with a chattering and gesticulating tide, the streets were loud with traffic, the clatter of trains, the heavy grinding of buses, the spiteful little horns of innumerable small taxis. But over all, over the opulence of the mown fields, and the untidy and distressful throngings of the towns, hung this high, sad light of evening.

A stranger, a visitor from some newer and more exultant earth—an American, perhaps—had he seen this coast thus for the first time, might have imagined the land as inhabited by a race far different from the one that really lived here: he would have felt the opulent austerity of this earth under its dying light, and he would have been deeply troubled by it.

For such a visitor, disturbed by the profound and subtle melancholy of this scene, for which his own experience had given him no adequate understanding or preparation, because it was steeped in peace without hope, in beauty without joy, in tranquil and brooding resignation without exultancy, the sight of the ship, as she lay now, immense and immovable at her anchor, would have pierced him suddenly with a thrill of victory, a sudden renewal of his faith and hope, a belief in the happy destiny of life.

She lay there, an alien presence in those waters; she had the reality of magic, the reality that is so living and magnificent that it seems unreal. She was miraculous and true—as one looked at her, settled like some magic luminosity upon that mournful coast, a strong cry of exultancy rose up in one's throat: the sight of the ship was as if a man's mistress had laid her hand upon his loins.

The ship was now wholly anchored: she lay there in the water with the living stillness of all objects that were made to move. Although entirely motionless, outwardly as fixed and permanent as any of the headlands of the coast, the story of her power and speed was legible in every line. She glowed and pulsed with the dynamic secret of life, and although her great sides towered immense and silent as a cliff, although the great plates of her hull seemed to reach down and to be founded in the sea's bed, and only the quietly flowing waters seemed to move and eddy softly at her sides, she yet had legible upon her the story of a hundred crossings, the memory of strange seas, of suns and moons and many different lights, the approach of April on far coasts, the change of wars and histories, and the completed dramas of all her voyages, charactered by the phantoms of many thousand passengers, the life, the hate, the love, the bitterness, the jealousy, the intrigue of six-day worlds, each one complete and separate in itself, which only a ship can have, which only the sea can bound, which only the earth can begin or end.

She glowed with the radiance of all her brilliant and luminous history; and besides this, she was literally a visitant from a new world. The stranger from the new world who saw the ship would also instantly have seen this. She had been built several years after the war and was entirely a product of European construction, engineering, navigation, and diplomacy. But her spirit, the impulse that communicated itself in each of her lines, was not European, but American. It is Europeans, for the most part, who have constructed these great ships, but without America they have no meaning. These ships are alive with the supreme ecstasy of the modern world, which is the voyage to America. There is no other experience that is remotely comparable to it, in its sense of joy, its exultancy, its drunken and magnificent hope which, against reason and knowledge, soars into a heaven of fabulous conviction, which believes in the miracle and sees it invariably achieved.

In this soft, this somewhat languid air, the ship glowed like an immense and brilliant jewel. All of her lights were on, they burned row by row straight across her 900 feet of length, with the small, hard twinkle of cut gems: it was as if the vast, black cliff of her hull, which strangely suggested the glittering night-time cliff of the fabulous city that was her destination, had been sown with diamonds.

And above this, her decks were ablaze with light. Her enormous superstructure with its magnificent frontal sweep, her proud breast which was so full of power and speed, her storied decks and promenades as wide as city streets, the fabulous variety and opulence of her public rooms, her vast lounges and salons, her restaurants, grills, and cafés, her libraries, writing-rooms, ballrooms, swimming-pools, her imperial suites with

broad beds, private decks, sitting-rooms, gleaming baths
—all of this, made to move upon the stormy seas, leaning against eternity and the gray welter of the Atlantic
at twenty-seven knots an hour, tenanted by the ghosts,
impregnated by the subtle perfumes of thousands of
beautiful and expensive women, alive with the memory
of the silken undulance of their long backs, with the
naked, living velvet of their shoulders as they paced
down the decks at night—all of this, with the four great
funnels that in the immense drive and energy of their
slant were now cut sharp and dark against the evening
sky, burned with a fierce, exultant vitality in the soft
melancholy of this coast.

The ship struck joy into the spinal marrow. In her
intense reality she became fabulous, a visitant from
another world, a creature monstrous and magical with
life, a stranger, seeming strange, to these melancholy
coasts, for she was made to glitter in the hard, sharp
air of a younger, more exultant land.

She was made also to quarter on the coasts of all the
earth, to range powerfully on the crest and ridge of the
globe, sucking continents towards her, devouring sea
and land; she was made to enter European skies like
some stranger from another world, to burn strangely
and fabulously in the dull, gray air of Europe, to pulse
and glow under the soft, wet European sky. But she
was only a marvellous stranger there; she was a bright,
jewelled thing; she came definitely, indubitably, won-
derfully from but one place on earth, and in only that
one place could she be fully seen and understood, in

only that one place could she slide in to her appointed and imperial setting.

That place was America: that place was the reaches to the American coast: that place was the approaches to the American continent. That place, finally, and absolutely, was the port whither she was bound—the fabulous rock of life, the proud, masted city of the soaring towers, which was flung with a lion's port into the maw of ocean. And as the Americans who were now approaching the ship in the puffing little tender saw this mark upon her, they looked at her and knew her instantly; they felt a qualm along their loins, their flesh stirred.

"Oh, look!" cried a woman suddenly, pointing to the ship whose immense and glittering side now towered over them. "Isn't that lovely! God, but she's big! How do you suppose we're ever going to find the ocean?"

"The first thing I'm going to do, darling, is find my bed," said her companion, in a tone of languorous weariness. A tall and sensual-looking Jewess, she was seated on a pile of baggage, smoking a cigarette, her long legs indolently crossed: indifferently, with smouldering and arrogant glances, she surveyed the crowd of passengers on the tender.

The other woman could not be still: her rosy face was burning with the exciement of the voyage, she kept slipping the ring on and off her finger nervously, and moving around at her brisk little step among the heaped-up piles of baggage.

"Oh, here!" she cried out suddenly in great excitement, pointing to a bag buried at the bottom of one of the piles. "Oh, here!" she cried again to the general public. "This one's mine! Where are the others? Can't you find the others for me?" she said in a sharp, protesting voice to one of the porters, a little, brawny man with sprouting mustaches. "Hey?" she said, lifting her small hand complainingly to her ear as he answered her in a torrent of reassuring French. She turned to her companion protestingly:

"I can't get them to do anything. They don't pay a bit of attention to what I say! I can't find my trunk and two of my bags. I think it's the most dreadful thing I ever heard of. Don't you? Hey?" again she lifted her little hand to her ear, for she was somewhat deaf: her small, rosy face was crimson with excitement and earnestness—in her tone, her manner, her indignation, there was something irresistibly comic, and suddenly her companion began to laugh.

"Oh, Esther!" she said. "Lord!" and then paused abruptly, as if there were no more to say.

Esther was fair; she was fair; she had dove's eyes.

Now the woman's lovely face, like a rarer, richer, and more luminous substance, was glowing among all the other faces of the travellers, which, as the tender circled and came in close below the ship, were fixed with a single intentness upon the great hull that loomed over them with its overpowering immensity.

The great ship cast over them all her mighty spell:

most of these people had made many voyages, yet the
great ship caught them up again in her magic glow,
she possessed and thrilled them with her presence as if
they had been children. The travellers stood there silent
and intent as the little boat slid in beside the big one,
they stood there with uplifted faces; and for a moment
it was strange and sad to see them thus, with loneliness
and longing in their eyes. Their faces made small, lifted
whitenesses; they shone in the gathering dark with a
luminous glimmer: there was something small, naked
and lonely in the glimmer of those faces, around them
was the immense eternity of sea and death. They heard
time.

For if, as men be dying, they can pluck one moment
from the darkness into which their sense is sinking, if
one moment in all the dark and mysterious forest
should then live, it might well be the memory of such
a moment as this which, although lacking in logical
meaning, burns for an instant in the dying memory as
a summary and a symbol of man's destiny on earth.
The fading memory has forgotten what was said then
by the passengers, the thousand tones and shadings of
the living moment are forgotten, but drenched in the
strange, brown light of time, the scene glows again for
an instant with an intent silence: darkness has fallen
upon the eternal earth, the great ship like a monstrous
visitant blazes on the waters, and on the tender the faces
of the travellers are lifted up like flowers in a kind of
rapt and mournful ecstasy—they are weary of travel,
they have wandered in strange cities among strange

tongues and faces, and they have left not even the
print of their foot in any town.

Their souls are naked and alone, and they are
strangers upon the earth, and many of them long for
a place where those weary of travel may find rest, where
those who are tired of searching may cease to search,
where there will be peace and quiet living, and no
desire. Where shall the weary find peace? Upon what
shore will the wanderer come home at last? When shall
it cease—the blind groping, the false desires, the fruit-
less ambitions that grow despicable as soon as they are
reached, the vain contest with phantoms, the maddening and agony of the brain and spirit in all the rush
and glare of living, the dusty tumult, the grinding, the
shouting, the idiot repetition of the streets, the sterile
abundance, the sick gluttony, and the thirst which goes
on drinking?

Out of one darkness the travellers have come to be
taken into another, but for a moment one sees their
faces, awful and still, all uplifted towards the ship.
This is all: their words have vanished, all memory of
the movements they made then has also vanished: one
remembers only their silence and their still faces lifted
in the phantasmal light of lost time; one sees them
ever, still and silent, as they slide from darkness on the
river of time; one sees them waiting at the ship's great
side, all silent and all damned to die, with their grave,
white faces lifted in a single supplication to the ship,
and towards the silent row of passengers along the deck,
who for a moment return their gaze with the same

grave and tranquil stare. That silent meeting is a summary of all the meetings of men's lives: in the silence one hears the slow, sad breathing of humanity, one knows the human destiny.

"Oh, look!" the woman cried again. "Oh, see! Was ever anything more beautiful?" The ship's great beetling cliff swept sheer above her. She turned the small, flushed flower of her face and saw the slant and reach and swell of the great prow, and music filled her. She lifted the small, flushed flower of her face and saw the many men, so little, so lonely, silent, and intent, that bent above her, looking from the ship's steep rail. She turned and saw the people all around her, the swift weave and patterned shifting of the forms, and she saw light then, ancient fading light, that fell upon the coasts of evening, and quiet waters reddened by fading day, and heard the unearthly creakings of a gull; and wonder filled her. And the strange and mortal ache of beauty, the anguish to pronounce what never could be spoken, to grasp what never could be grasped, to hold and keep forever what was gone the moment she put her hand upon it——

"Oh, these people here," she cried in a high tone— "The ship! . . . My God, the things that I could tell you all!" she cried indignantly. "The things I know— the things I have inside me here!"—she struck herself upon the breast with one clenched hand—"the way things are, the way they happen, and the beauty of the clear design—and no one ever asks me!" she cried out indignantly. "This wonderful thing is going on inside me all the time—and no one ever wants to know the way it happens!"—and stood staring at her friend accusingly a moment, a little figure of indignant loveliness until, becoming aware of people's smiles and her companion's laughter, her own face was suddenly suffused, and, casting back her head, she was swept with gale-like merriment—a full, rich, woman's yell of triumph and delight.

And yet, even as she laughed, she was pierced again by the old ache of wonder, the old anguish of unspoken desire, and saw the many men, so lonely, silent, and intent, the ship immense and sudden there above her in old evening light, and so—remembering, "Can'st thou draw out leviathan with an hook? or his tongue with a cord which thou lettest down?"—was still with wonder.

Ah, strange and beautiful, the woman thought, how can I longer bear this joy intolerable, the music of this great song unpronounceable, the anguish of this glory unimaginable, which fills my life to bursting and which will not let me speak! It is too hard, too hard, and not to be endured, to feel the great vine welling in my heart, the wild, strange music swelling in my throat, the triumph of that final perfect song that aches forever there just at the gateway of my utterance—and that has no tongue to speak! O magic moment, that are so perfect, unknown, and inevitable, to stand here at this ship's great side, here at the huge last edge of evening and return, with this still wonder in my heart and knowing only that somehow we are fulfilled of you, O time! And see, how gathered there against the rail high over us, there at the ship's great side, are all the people, silent, lonely, and so beautiful; strange brothers of this voyage, chance phantoms of the bitter briefness of our days—and you, oh youth—for now she saw him there for the first time—who bend there, lone and lean and secret, at the rail of night, why are you there alone while these, your fellows, wait? . . . Ah secret and alone, she thought—how lean with hunger, and how fierce with pride, and how burning with impossible desire he bends there at the rail of night—and he is wild and young and foolish and forsaken, and his eyes are starved, his soul is parched with thirst, his heart is famished with a hunger that cannot be fed, and he leans there on the rail and dreams great dreams, and he is mad for love and is athirst for glory, and he is so cruelly mistaken— and so right! . . . Ah, see, she thought, how that wild light flames there upon his brow—how bright, how burning and how beautiful—O passionate and proud! —how like the wild, lost soul of youth you are, how like my wild lost father who will not return!

He turned, and saw her then, and so finding her, was lost, and so losing self, was found, and so seeing her, saw for a fading moment only the pleasant image of the woman that perhaps she was, and that life saw. He never knew: he knew only that from that moment his spirit was impaled upon the knife of love. From that moment on he never was again to lose her utterly, never to wholly re-possess unto himself the lonely, wild integrity of youth which had been his. At that instant of their meeting, that proud inviolability of youth was broken, not to be restored. At that moment of their meeting she got into his life by some dark magic, and before he knew it, he had her beating in the pulses of his blood—somehow thereafter—how he never knew—to steal into the conduits of his heart, and to inhabit the lone, inviolable tenement of his one life; so, like love's great thief, to steal through all the adyts of his soul, and to become a part of all he did and said and was—through this invasion so to touch all loveliness that he might touch, through this strange and subtle stealth of love henceforth to share all that he might feel or make or dream, until there was for him no beauty that she did not share, no music that did not have her being in it, no horror, madness, hatred, sickness of the soul, or grief unutterable, that was not somehow consonant to her single image and her million forms—and no final freedom and release, bought through the incalculable expenditure of blood and anguish and despair, that would not bear upon its brow forever the deep scar, upon its sinews the old mangling chains, of love.

After all the blind, tormented wanderings of youth, that woman would become his heart's centre and the target of his life, the image of immortal one-ness that again collected him to one, and hurled the whole collected passion, power and might of his one life into the blazing certitude, the immortal governance and unity, of love.

Herrick, Crashaw, Carew

O F HERRICK, sealed of the tribe of Ben, he knew much more. The poetry sang itself. It was, he thought later, the most perfect and unfailing lyrical voice in the language—a clean, sweet, small, unfaltering note. It is done with the incomparable ease of an inspired child. The young men and women of our century have tried to recapture it, as they have tried to recapture Blake and, a little more successfully, Donne.

> Here a little child I stand
> Heaving up my either hand;
> Cold as paddocks though they be,
> Here I lift them up to Thee,
> For a benison to fall
> On our meat and on us all.   Amen.

There was nothing beyond this—nothing that surpassed it in precision, delicacy, and wholeness.

Their names dropped musically like small fat birdnotes through the freckled sunlight of a young world: prophetically he brooded on the sweet lost bird-cries of their names, knowing they never would return. Herrick, Crashaw, Carew, Suckling, Campion, Lovelace, Dekker. O sweet content, O sweet, O sweet content!

May Morning in the Park

S O WE went on up that hill and coasted down the next, and now we really seemed to fly. It was like soaring through the air, or finding wings you never knew you had before. It was like something we had always known about and dreamed of finding, and now we had it like a dream come true. And I suppose we must have gone the whole way round the park from one end to another, but none of us really knew how far we went or where we were going. It was like that kind of flight you make in dreams, and sure enough, just like something you are waiting for in a dream, we came tearing around a curve in the road and there before us we could see the same hansom we had tried to pass upon the hill. And the minute that I saw it I knew that it was bound to happen, it seemed too good to be true, and yet I had felt sure all the time that it was going to turn out just this way. And that was the way it was with all of us, we threw back our heads and roared with laughter, we yelled and waved our hands at all the people in the cab, we went tearing by them as if they were rooted to the earth, and as we passed them Daddy turned and shouted back at them, "Cheer up, my friends, they also serve who only stand and wait."

So we passed them by and left them far behind us and they were lost; and now there was nothing all around us but the night, the blazing stars, the lilac darkness in the park, and God! but it was beautiful. It was just the beginning of May and all the leaves and buds were coming out, they had that tender feathery look, and there was just a little delicate shaving of moon in the sky, and it was so cool and lovely, with the smell of the leaves, and the new grass, and all the flowers bursting from the earth till you could hear them grow: it seemed to me the loveliest thing that I had ever known, and when I looked at my father, his eyes were full of tears and he cried out, "Glory! Oh, glory! Glory!" and then he began in his magnificent voice, "What a piece of work is a man! how noble in reason! how infinite in faculty! in form and moving how express and admirable! in action how like an angel! in apprehension how like a god!"

And the words were so lovely, the music was so grand, that somehow it made me want to cry, and when he had finished he cried out, "Glory!" once again, and I

[313]

saw his wild and beautiful brow there in the darkness, and I turned my eyes up toward the sky and there were the tragic and magnificent stars, and a kind of fate was on his head and in his eyes, and suddenly as I looked at him I knew that he was going to die.

And he cried, "Glory! Glory!" and we rode all through the night, and round and round the park, and then dawn came, and all of the birds began to sing. And now the bird-song broke in the first light, and suddenly I heard each sound the bird-song made. It came to me like music I had always heard, it came to me like music I had always known, the sounds of which I never yet had spoken, and now I heard the music of each sound as clear and bright as gold, and the music of each sound was this: at first it rose above me like a flight of shot, and then I heard the sharp, fast skaps of sound the bird-song made. And now they were smooth drops and nuggets of bright gold, and now with chittering bicker and fast-fluttering skirrs of sound the palmy, honied bird-cries came. And now the bird-tree sang, all filled with lutings in bright air; the thrum, the lark's wing, and tongue-trilling chirrs arose. And now the little brainless cries arose, with liquorous, liquefied lutings, with lirruping chirp, plumbellied smoothness, sweet lucidity. And now I heard the rapid kweet-kweet-kweet-kweet-kweet of homely birds, and then their pwee-pwee-pwee: others had thin metallic tongues, a sharp cricketing stitch, and high shrew's caws, with eerie rasp, with harsh, far calls—these were the sounds the bird-cries made. All birds that are awoke in the park's

woodland tangles; and above them passed the whirr
of hidden wings, the strange lost cry of the unknown
birds in full light now in the park, the sweet confusion
of their cries was mingled. "Sweet is the breath of
morn, her rising sweet with charm of earliest birds,"
and it was just like that, and the sun came up, and it
was like the first day of the world, and that was the
year before he died, and I think we were staying at
Bella's then, but maybe we were staying at the old hotel,
or perhaps we had already moved to Auntie Kate's:
we moved around so much, we lived so many places, it
seems so long ago, that when I try to think about it
now it gets confused and I cannot remember.

Food

I T WAS such a kitchen as he had never seen before—
a kitchen such as he had never dreamed possible.
In its space, its order, its astounding cleanliness, it
had the beauty of a great machine—a machine of
tremendous power, fabulous richness and complexity—
which in its ordered magnificence, its vast readiness,
had the clear and glittering precision of a geometric
pattern. Even the stove—a vast hooded range as large
as those in a great restaurant—glittered with the
groomed perfection of a racing motor. There was, as
well, an enormous electric stove that was polished like
a silver ornament, the pots and pans were hung in
gleaming rows, in vast but orderly profusion ranging
from great copper kettles big enough to roast an ox to
little pans and skillets just large enough to poach an egg,
but all hung there in regimented order, instant readiness, shining like mirrors, scrubbed and polished into

gleaming disks, the battered cleanliness of well-used copper, seasoned iron and heavy steel.

The great cupboards were crowded with huge stacks of gleaming china ware and crockery, enough to serve the needs of a hotel. And the long kitchen table, as well as the chairs and woodwork of the room, was white and shining as a surgeon's table: the sinks and drains were blocks of creamy porcelain, clean scrubbed copper, shining steel.

It would be impossible to describe in detail the lavish variety, the orderly complexity, the gleaming cleanliness of that great room, but the effect it wrought upon his senses was instant and overwhelming. It was one of the most beautiful, spacious, thrilling, and magnificently serviceable rooms that he had ever seen: everything in it was designed for use, and edged with instant readiness; there was not a single thing in the room that was not needed, and yet its total effect was to give one a feeling of power, space, comfort, rightness and abundant joy.

The pantry shelves were crowded to the ceiling with the growing treasure of a lavish victualling—an astounding variety and abundance of delicious foods, enough to stock a grocery store, or to supply an Arctic expedition —but the like of which he had never seen, or dreamed of, in a country house before.

Everything was there, from the familiar staples of a cook's necessities to every rare and toothsome dainty that the climates and the markets of the earth produce. There was food in cans, and food in tins, and food in crocks, and food in bottles. There were—in addition to such staple products of the canning art as corn, tomatoes, beans and peas, pears, plums and peaches—such rarer relishes, as herrings, sardines, olives, pickles, mustard, anchovies. There were boxes of glacéd crystalline fruits from California, and little wickered jars of sharp-spiced ginger fruit from China: there were expensive jellies green as emerald, red as rubies, smoother than whipped cream, there were fine oils and vinegars in bottles, and jars of pungent relishes of every sort, and boxes of assorted spices. There was everything that one could think of, and everywhere there was evident the same scrubbed and gleaming cleanliness with which the kitchen shone, but here there was, as well, that pungent, haunting, spicy odor that pervades the atmosphere of pantries—a haunting and nostalgic fusion of delicious smells whose exact quality it is impossible to define, but which has in it the odors of cinnamon, pepper, cheese, smoked ham, and cloves.

Food! Food, indeed! The great icebox was crowded with such an assortment of delicious foods as he had not seen in many years: just to look at it made the mouth begin to water, and aroused the pangs of a hunger so ravenous and insatiate that it was almost more painful than the pangs of bitter want. One was so torn with desire and greedy gluttony as he looked at the maddening plenty of that feast that his will was rendered almost impotent. Even as the eye glistened and the mouth began to water at the sight of a noble roast of beef, all crisp and crackly in its cold brown succulence, the attention was diverted to a plump broiled chicken, whose brown and crackly tenderness fairly seemed to beg for the sweet and savage pillage of the tooth. But now a pungent and exciting fragrance would assail the nostrils: it was the smoked pink slices of an Austrian ham —should it be brawny bully beef, now, or the juicy breast of a white tender pullet, or should it be the smoky pungency, the half-nostalgic savor of the Austrian ham? Or that noble dish of green lima beans, now already beautifully congealed in their pervading film of melted butter; or that dish of tender stewed young cucumbers; or those tomato slices, red and thick and ripe, and heavy as a chop; or that dish of cold asparagus, say; or that dish of corn; or, say, one of those musty fragrant, deep-ribbed cantaloupes, chilled to the heart, now, in all their pink-fleshed taste and ripeness; or a round thick slab cut from the red ripe heart of that great watermelon; or a bowl of those red raspberries, most luscious and most rich with sugar, and a bottle of that thick rich cream which filled one whole compartment of that treasure-chest of gluttony, or——

What shall it be now? What shall it be? A snack! A snack!—before we prowl the meadows of the moon tonight, and soak our hearts in the moonlight's magic and the visions of our youth—what shall it be before we prowl the meadows of the moon? Oh, it shall be a snack, a snack—hah! hah!—it shall be nothing but a snack because—hah! hah!—you understand, we are not hungry and it is not well to eat too much before retiring— so we'll just investigate the icebox as we have done so oft at midnight in America—and we are the moon's man, boys—and all that it will be, I do assure you, will be something swift and quick and ready, something instant and felicitous, and quite delicate and dainty— just a snack!

I think—now let me see—h'm, now!—well, perhaps I'll have a slice or two of that pink Austrian ham that smells so sweet and pungent and looks so pretty and so delicate there in the crisp garlands of the parsley leaf!— and yes, perhaps, I'll have a slice of this roast beef, as well—h'm now!—yes, I think that's what I'm going to do—say a slice of red rare meat there at the centre—ah-h! there you are! yes, that's the stuff, that does quite nicely, thank you—with just a trifle of that crisp brown crackling there to oil the lips and make its passage easy, and a little of that cold but brown and oh—most—brawny gravy—and, yes, sir! I think I *will*, now that it occurs to me, a slice of that plump chicken—some white meat, thank you, at the breast—ah, there it is!—how sweetly doth the noble fowl submit to the swift and keen persuasion of the knife—and now, perhaps, just for our diet's healthy balance, a spoonful of those lima beans, as gay as April and as sweet as butter, a tomato slice or two, a speared forkful of those thin-sliced cucumbers —ah! what a delicate and toothsome pickle they do make—what sorcerer invented them, a little corn perhaps, a bottle of this milk, a pound of butter and that crusty loaf of bread—and even this moon-haunted wilderness were paradise enow—with just a snack—a snack —a snack——

The Hills of Home

AROUND them, above them, below them—from the living and shining air of autumn, from the embrowned autumnal earth, from the great shapes of the hills behind them with their molten mass of color—dull browns, rich bitter reds, dark bronze, and mellow yellow—from the raw crude clay of the piedmont earth and the great brown stubble of the cotton fields—from a thousand impalpable and unutterable things, there came this glorious breath of triumph and delight. It was late October, there was a smell of smoke upon the air, an odor of burning leaves, the barking of a dog, a misty red, a pollenated gold in the rich, fading, sorrowful, and exultant light of the day,—and far off, a sound of great wheels pounding on a rail, the wailing whistle, and the tolling bell of a departing train.

And finally, the immortal visage of the earth itself

with the soaring and limitless undulations of its blue ranges, the great bulk of the autumn hills, immense and near, the rugged, homely, and familiar trees—the pines, oaks, chestnuts, maples, locusts—the homely look of the old red clay—the unforgettable and indescribable naturalness of that earth—with its rudeness, wildness, richness, rawness, ugliness, fathomless mystery and utter familiarity, and finally the lonely, haunting, and enchanted music that it made—the strange spirit of time and solitude that hovered above it eternally, and which can never be described, but which may be evoked by the sound of a cowbell broken by the wind in distant valleys, the lonely whistle of a departing train, or simply a sinuous gust of wind that smokes its way across coarse mountain grasses when spring comes—all this, which Eugene had felt and known in his childhood, and yet had never had a tongue to utter, he seemed now to know and understand so well that he had himself become its tongue and utterance, the more its child because he had been so long away from it, the more its eye because he now saw it again as it must have seemed to the first men who ever saw it, with the eyes of discovery, love, and recognition.

Feb 27 '52

Oct 24 '52

May 28 '53